INTRODUCTION

Thank you for your purchase of THE CHESS TACTICS WORKBOOK, 4th edition. What makes this book different from the many other tactics books on the market is that it was written by a classroom teacher for other teachers. All the pages are formatted with a heading to easily identify the concepts the puzzles are designed to teach.

This edition includes an introduction to the game as well as 14 puzzle pages taken from *Scholar's Mate*, published by The Chess'n Math Association, Canada's national scholastic organization. Changes have also been made to improve the quality, appearance and accuracy of the material.

The worksheets take a student from the fundamentals of mate to the basic tactical elements, through more advanced tactical concepts, then into mating attacks and combinations that employ those elements and concepts.

Materials in this book have been arranged to teach chess tactics in a progressive fashion. An emphasis is placed on the concept of mate and the ability to search for good moves. (How often do your students overlook simple mates?) Young students need to learn how to add layers to the depth and width of their search; hence, the orderly increase in difficulty of the problems presented.

When designing a program or course of study for students in grades 2 through 9, the best two suggestions I can give a fellow coach are to keep the lectures short (20 minutes or 1/3 of your time) and teach the mechanics of winning (combinations and endgame technique). Students should study opening principles and the concepts of positional chess (20%), endgame methods (30%), in addition to the tactical methods (50%) in this workbook.

COVER ART

The cover was designed by the award-winning artist and chess player, Clint Cearley of Weatherford, Texas.

THE AUTHOR

I have served on the Scholastic Committee of the U.S. Chess Federation as well as Scholastic Coordinator for Texas and South California for many years, and I have taught numerous summer camps and provided in-service training to teachers in the Tarrant county area.

DEDICATION

The material in this book and my love of chess were developed in Kern County California while teaching at Bakersfield High School. I had the unique pleasure of coaching Thorner Elementary (K-3 section) and Bakersfield H.S. to their respective State Championships in 1993 and helping Mr. Greg Hauss of Owens School as co-founder of the Kern County Chess Federation (KCCF), a coalition of educators and volunteers dedicated to academic enrichment through chess. The KCCF sponsored in-service training for teachers and hosted a full schedule of tournaments for students in the Kern County area. This book is dedicated to my friends in California and the many wonderful people involved in scholastic chess throughout North America whom I have met and worked with in the past.

USE OF THIS MATERIAL . . .

is restricted to the private use of the purchaser. Limited rights to reproduce the lessons are granted to teachers for use in their classrooms only. This book is inexpensive enough that it might be easier to buy in quantity so that each student can have his own copy. Call the distributor or visit the following websites for quantity discounts:

CHESS IN EDUCATION
(504) 208-9596
www.chessineducation.com
www.cajunchess.com

(Reprint July 2017)

TABLE OF CONTENTS

Basic mating patterns for pieces and pawns are tested. Mate is the object of the game and the number one threat in the arsenal of chess tactics.

Students learn the basic weapons of attack; pins, skewers, double attacks, discovered attacks, pawn promotion, and material threats.

Decoys, cross-pins,pawn breakthroughs and other tactical devices are combined and used to win material and checkmate the opponent. Students learn to think ahead and look at their opponents responses. Special answer sheet masters are provided at the back of the book.

Queen sacrifices, double attacks, discovered & double checks, rook & minor piece mates, pawn mates and attacks on the castled king

More combination training and pattern recognition to help hunt down the enemy king.

The students' logic tree branches out as the complexity of the forced mate increases.

A special section with thirty complete games from the Giucco Piano(Italian) opening and a diagram of the position where forced mate occurs.

All problems are 1 or 2 move combinations that result in either a win of material or checkmate.

All problems are 3-move combinations that result in checkmate.

Train your brain as the logic becomes more difficult.

Test your knowledge and find a winning line.

Some unique problems from *Scholar's Mate*, the Canadian Chess Magazine for kids.

The Game of Chess

What is Chess?

Chess is a war game that was invented over 1300 years ago in India. We don't know if the game was invented to train warriors in the subtleties of warfare or a civilized way for kingdoms to settle their differences. What we do know is that the game achieved great popularity as it spread to other cultures around the world.

The game of chess was brought to the West by the crusaders and the traders who dealt in silk, spices, and other treasures from the East. The Moors of North Africa and the Persians were two groups of people who helped bring the game to Europe.

Chess is a battle between two armies; one light in color and one dark. Each army is made up of 16 pieces that include a King, 1 Queen, 2 Rooks, 2 Bishops, 2 Knights, and 8 Pawns. The battlefield is a large square made up of 64 smaller squares arranged in an 8x8 grid of alternating dark and light squares.

What Is the Object of the game?

The object of the game is to checkmate your opponent. A checkmate happens when the enemy King is under attack and cannot get out of check on his next move. There are other ways that a game of chess can end but that is a topic for a later lesson. To show you a checkmate we first need to learn more about the board and the pieces.

The Board and the Pieces

Diagram 1a shows the board. The symbol for each piece is shown in diagram 1b. The correct starting setup of the pieces is shown in diagram 1c. Notice that when the pieces are set up correctly there is a white square in the lower right hand corner and the Queens are on a square that matches their color. An easy phrase to remember when setting up the board is "white to the right and Queen on color." Finally, each square on our battlefield is named using a letter and a number. White's King, for example, is on square e1.

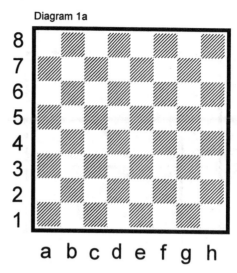

Diagram 1a

Diagram 1b

	BLACK	WHITE
King	♚	♔
Queen	♛	♕
Rook	♜	♖
Bishop	♝	♗
Knight	♞	♘
Pawn	♟	♙

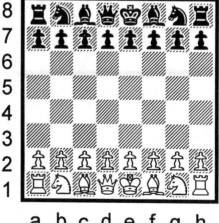

Diagram 1c

More about the board

We also call the horizontal rows—ranks; vertical rows—files; and the lines of squares of the same color, that are connected corner to corner, diagonals.

Diagram 2

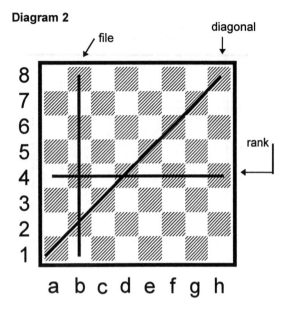

The Pawn

A pawn can move one or two squares on its first move. Every pawn gets that choice. After a pawn makes its first move it can only advance one square at a time. Pawns can only move forward (diagram 3).

Diagram 3

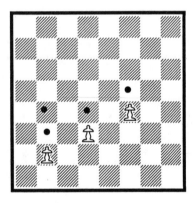

The pawn on the left hasn't moved. It can advance one or two squares. The two pawns on the right have already moved. They can only advance one square at a time.

Diagram 4

The Pawn is unique because it is the only piece in chess that attacks differently than it moves. It attacks the two squares diagonally in front of the square it is on (diagram 4).

Capturing

Diagram 5a -- before

The Pawn attacks the Rook. It doesn't attack the Bishop or Rook.

Diagram 5b

The pawn captures the Rook.

When pawns reach the end of the board, or the 8th rank, they receive a battlefield promotion to a Knight, Bishop, Rook, or Queen. Of course, most people choose a queen because it is the most powerful piece. When a pawn is promoted it doesn't matter what has been captured. For Instance, it is customary to turn a rook upside down and pretend it is a queen if no more Queens are available. It may not happen in a real game, but it is possible to have 9 queens if all 8 pawns promote (diagram 6).

Diagram 6a -- before

The pawn can move to the 8th rank. White must promote to a Knight, Bishop, Rook, or Queen.

Diagram 6b -- After

The pawn moves forward and promotes to a Queen. It attacks the King on the same move. The King is in "check".

Pawns also have a special move called "**en passant**". It is a capture of an enemy pawn that is only possible when a pawn moves two squares on its first move through the square that an enemy pawn attacks (diagram 7)

Diagram 7a -- before

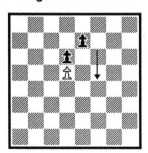

Diagram 7b -- during

Diagram 7c -- after

THE GAME OF CHESS
The Knight

The Knight moves in a pattern that looks like a small "L". It is also unique because it can jump over other pieces. That means that the Knight does not attack the squares in its path, only the squares that it can move to. Many beginners have trouble with the Knight because it does not move in a straight line. Pay particular attention to the Knight when looking for moves. As one grandmaster said: "He who masters Knights, masters chess!"

Diagram 8

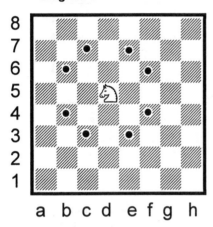

The Knight at d5 can move to any of the eight squares marked with a dot.

Diagram 9

The Knight at d5 attacks the pawn at c7 and the Queen at f6. The other pieces do not block the Knight because it has the power to jump over them. The Rook at e5 is safe from attack.

Diagram 10

The Knight captures the Queen at f6.

THE GAME OF CHESS
The Bishop

The Bishop moves on a diagonal in any direction. It cannot jump over anything. As long as the diagonal is clear it can move in that direction. It cannot "turn a corner" or change direction in one move. For example, it would take two moves for a Bishop at f1 to move to d5. A Bishop, like all the pieces in chess, captures by moving onto the square of the captured piece. The enemy piece, that was captured, is removed from the game.

Diagram 11

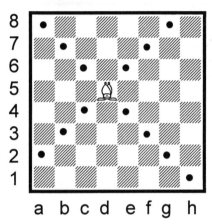

The Bishop at d5 can move to any of the 13 squares marked with a dot.

Diagram 12

The Bishop at c3 has the choice of capturing the Rook, Knight, or Bishop. It cannot capture the Queen at h8 because it is blocked by the pawn at f6.

Diagram 13

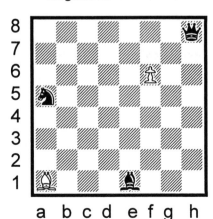

The Bishop has captured the Rook.

THE GAME OF CHESS
The Rook

The Rook moves in a straight line, vertically and horizontally, along the files and ranks. It can move in any direction as long as its path is not blocked. Like the Bishop, it captures along the same path that it moves on. The Rook moves onto the square of the captured piece which is removed from the board.

Diagram 14

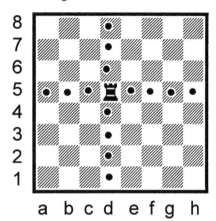

The Rook at d5 can move to any of the 14 squares marked with a dot.

Diagram 15

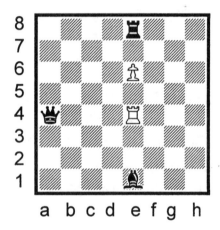

The Rook at e4 has the choice of capturing the Bishop or Queen. It cannot capture the Rook at e8 because it is blocked by the pawn at e6.

Diagram 16

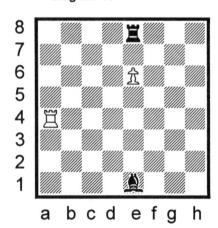

The Rook has captured the Queen at a4.

THE GAME OF CHESS
The Queen

The Queen has the combined moves of the Bishop and the Rook. It can move diagonally or along the ranks and files.

Diagram 17

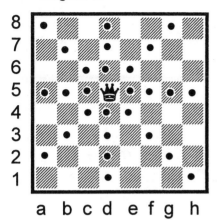

The Queen at d5 can move to any of the 27 squares marked with a dot.

Diagram 18

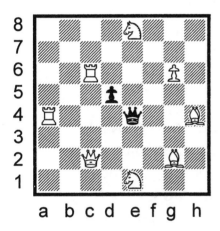

The black Queen at e4 attacks 7 different white pieces. It cannot capture the Rook at c6 because the pawn at d5 is blocking the attack.

Diagram 19

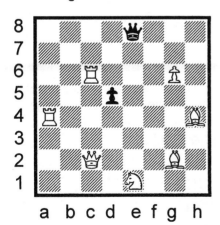

The Queen has captured the Knight at e8.

THE GAME OF CHESS
The King

The basic move of the King is simple. It can move one square in any direction. The King is restricted by the fact it can never move onto a square that is under attack by an enemy piece. When a King comes under attack we call that "check". The King must get out of check on his turn or the game ends. When the King has no way out of check the result is "checkmate" and the game is over.

Another situation that sometimes occurs late in a game is when the King, which is not in check, cannot move and the player whose turn it is has no other legat move. That situation is called stalemate.

Diagram 20

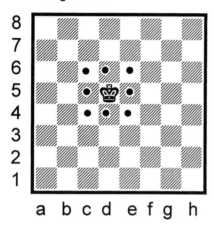

The King at d5 can move to any of the 8 squares marked with a dot.

Diagram 21

The King can only move to the three squares with a dot. The enemy Queen attacks the other squares surrounding the King.

Check

Check is an attack on the King. The Player who's King is in check must get the King out of check on the next turn. Any Other move would be illegal. If the King cannot be removed from check, the game is over. We have checkmate!

The Three Ways To Escape Check

1. Capture the Attacker
2. Block The Attacker
3. Move the King

Remember: Chess, like life is about making good choices. When your King comes under attack don't just grab the King and move it. You may have a choice about how to get out of check or where to move to. Evaluate those choices carefully because " **a piece touched is a piece moved**".

Page h

Diagram 22 -- before

The King is in check. It could move to one of the three squares with a dot but the best choice is to capture the Queen with the Rook.

Diagram 22 -- after

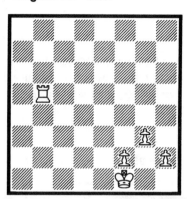

Block The Attacker

Diagram 23 -- before

The King is in check. The best choice is to block the attack with the Bishop. That prevents the Bishop from being captured by the Queen.

Diagram 23 -- after

Move The King

Diagram 24 -- before

The King is in check. White's only choice is to move the King. The King has sought shelter behind the pawns,

Diagram 24 -- after

THE GAME OF CHESS
The King--Checkmate

Checkmate occurs when the King cannot get out of check. That marks the end of the game. If you find yourself in a position to capture the enemy King on your turn hen an illegal move must have been made the move before. Remember, the King is never captured. Diagrams 25 & 26 are two examples of checkmate.

Diagram 25

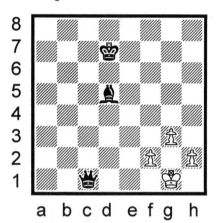

The King at g1 has no escape from the Queen's attack. The result is checkmate and Black wins the game.

Diagram 26

The black King is under attack by the Queen; it cannot move onto the squares (c7, d7, e7) controlled by the white King. It's Checkmate! And White wins.

Stalemate

In diagrams 27 & 28 it is black's turn to move. Notice that the King is not in check and that none of the other black soldiers can make a legal move. These are stalemates which are scored as tie games.

Diagram 27

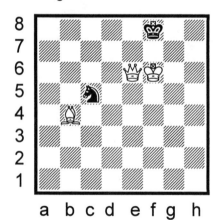

Diagram 28

THE GAME OF CHESS
The King--Castling

Castling is a special move for the King that also involves the Rook. The King moves two squares to the right or left from its starting square and the Rook is brought over the King to the square adjacent to the King. It is a simple move but very important because it moves the King to safety and moves the rook into a better position to find an open file for an attack on the enemy. Because of its importance there are several rules that restrict the move.

Castling

Diagram 29--before

Diagram 30--after

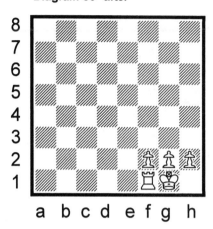

Restrictions on Castling
1) Castling must be the first move for the King and the Rook used to castle
2) All the squares between the King and Rook must be clear
3) It is illegal to castle to get out of check
4) It is illegal to castle through a square that is under attack

Diagram 30

White would like to castle to the left and capture the Knight but that is illegal. All the squares between the King and Rook must be clear.

Diagram 31

White can't castle. The King can't move through a square(f1) that is under attack.

Diagram 32

White can't castle. The King can't castle to get out of check.

THE GAME OF CHESS
Notation

It is recommended that chess players, especially young students, learn to record their moves on a scoresheet. Notation is a simple matter of writing down win an abbreviated code, the piece that moved and the square it moved to.

Name	Symbol
King	K
Queen	Q
Rook	R
Bishop	B
Knight	N
Pawn	p or (none)
Castling, Kingside	O-O
Castling, Queenside	O-O-O
Capture	x
Check	+
Checkmate	++
Good Move	!
Bad Move	?
Really Bad	??
Debatable	?!

Try playing through the sample game on page 133 to practice reading chess notation. Remember, the pawn moves are given simply as a square or are designated by a little letter. The move 1. e4 means that White moved the pawn in front of the King from e2 to e4.

Study Questions

1) How many moves will it take to move the Knight from a1 to a8?_____ List the moves:_____

2) Record a second Path the Knight could take:_____

3) How many moves will it take to move a Knight from a1 to h8?_____

4) What is the most powerful attacking piece in Chess? Why?

5) Which piece captures differently than it moves?

6) Which is the only piece that can jump over other pieces?

7) What is checkmate?

8) If a Knight was on square h1, how many squares would it attack?

9) If a Knight was on e5, how many squares would it attack?

10) List two reasons why castling is important?

Skill Building Activities

The Pawn game
Set up the pawns on their starting squares. White moves first and then Black. The first person to advance a pawn to the last rank wins the game. If either player runs out of legal moves before a pawn reaches the last rank the game is a tie.

Queen vs. Pawns
Play one Queen against 8 pawns starting from the original squares. The Player with the pawns starts first. If a pawn advances to the last rank, that player wins. If the Queen captures all the pawns before one of them promotes then the player with the Queen wins.

Checkmate with the Rook
(WHITE TO MOVE)

Diagram 1

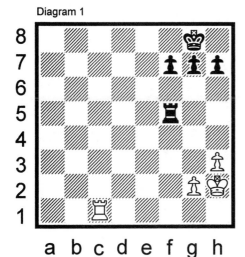

Diagram 2

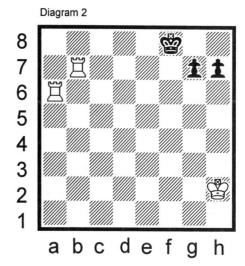

Diagram 3

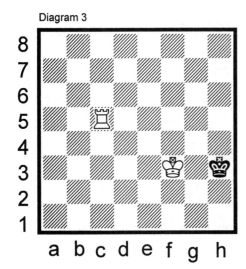

Diagram 4

Diagram 5

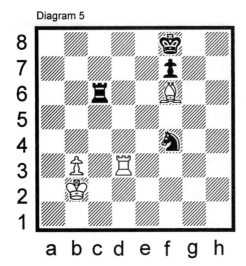

Diagram 6

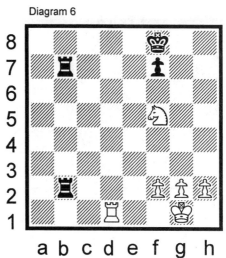

Checkmate In One Move
(WHITE TO MOVE)

Diagram 1

Diagram 2

Diagram 3

Diagram 4

Diagram 5

Diagram 6

Checkmate In One Move
(WHITE TO MOVE)

Diagram 1

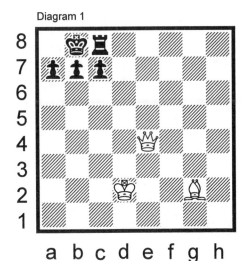

Diagram 2

Diagram 3

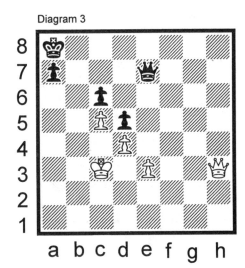

Diagram 4

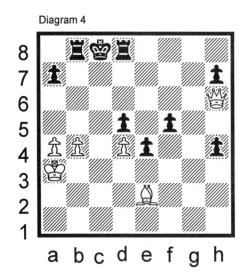

Diagram 5

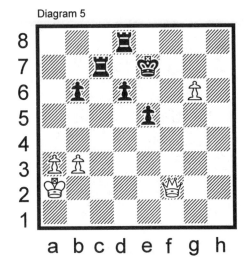

Diagram 6

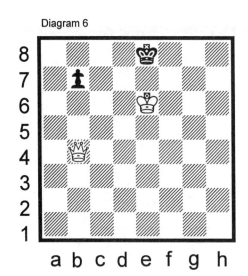

Page 3

Checkmate In One Move
(WHITE TO MOVE)

Diagram 1

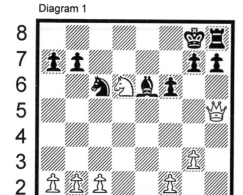

Diagram 2

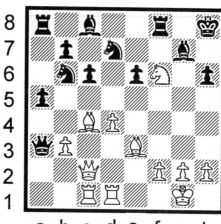

Diagram 3

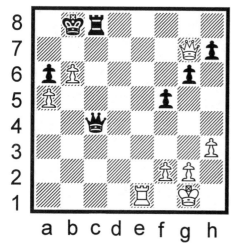

Diagram 4

Diagram 5

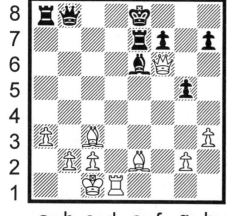

Diagram 6

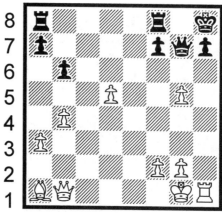

Checkmate In One Move
(WHITE TO MOVE)

Diagram 1

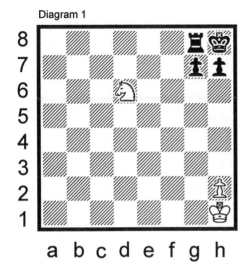

Diagram 2

Diagram 3

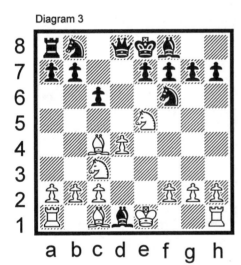

Diagram 4

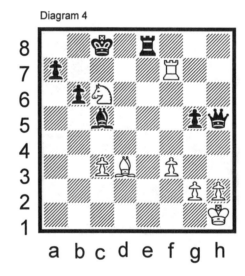

Diagram 5

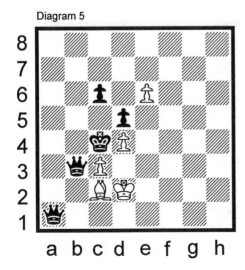

Diagram 6

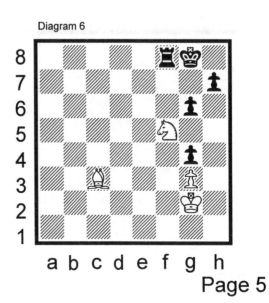

Checkmate In One Move

(WHITE TO MOVE)

Diagram 1

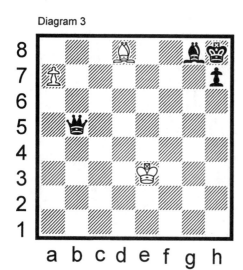

Diagram 2

Diagram 3

Diagram 4

Diagram 5

Diagram 6

Checkmate In One Move
(WHITE TO MOVE)

Diagram 1

Diagram 2

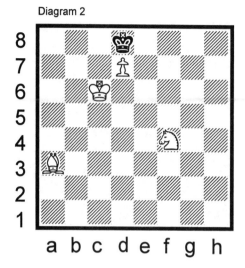

Diagram 3

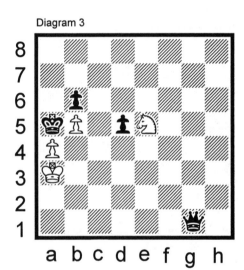

Diagram 4

Diagram 5

Diagram 6

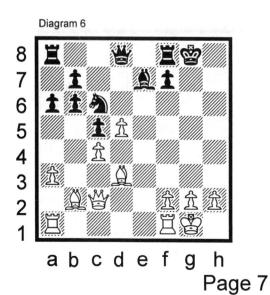

Checkmate In One Move
(WHITE TO MOVE)

Diagram 1

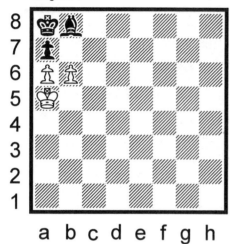

Diagram 2

Diagram 3

Diagram 4

Diagram 5

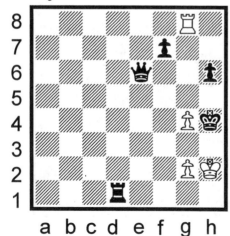

Diagram 6

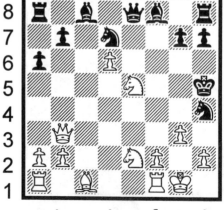

Checkmate In One Move
(WHITE TO MOVE)

Diagram 1

1.____

Diagram 2

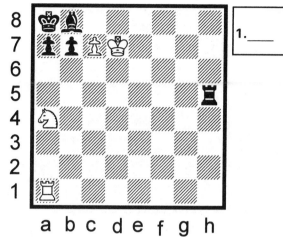

1.____

Diagram 3

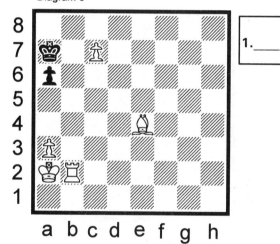

1.____

Diagram 4

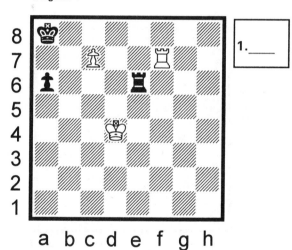

1.____

Diagram 5

1.____

Diagram 6

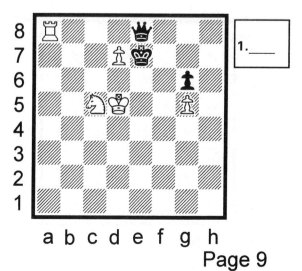

1.____

Checkmate In One Move
(WHITE TO MOVE)

Diagram 1

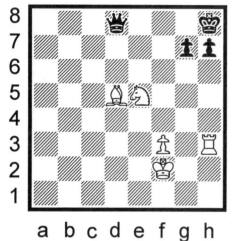

Diagram 2

Diagram 3

Diagram 4

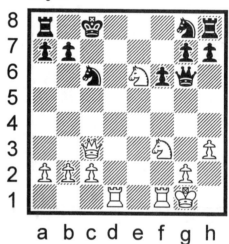

Diagram 5

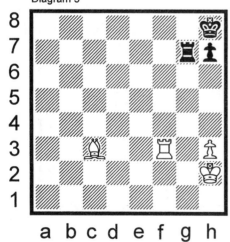

Diagram 6

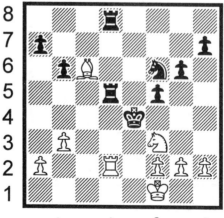

Checkmate In One Move
(White to Move)

Diagram 1
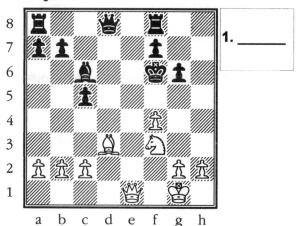

1. _____

Diagram 2
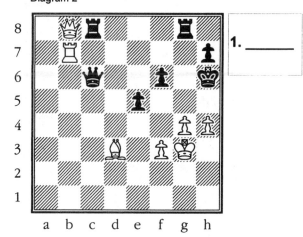

1. _____

Diagram 3
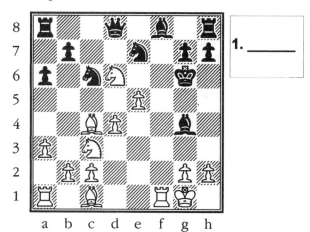

1. _____

Diagram 4
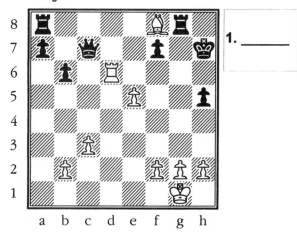

1. _____

Diagram 5
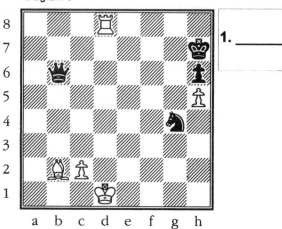

1. _____

Diagram 6
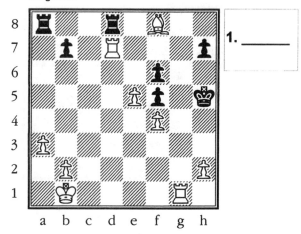

1. _____

Checkmate In One Move
(WHITE TO MOVE)

Diagram 1

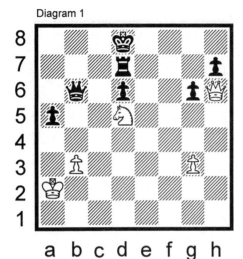

Diagram 2

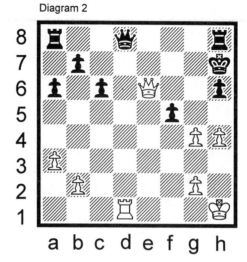

Diagram 3

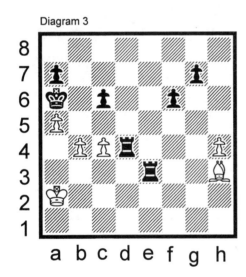

Diagram 4

Diagram 5

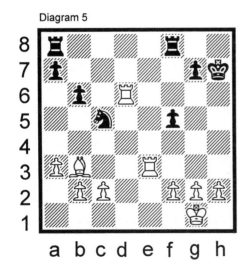

Diagram 6

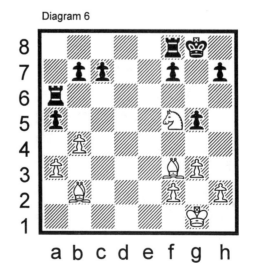

Need More Mate In One Problems? Go to pages 121-126.

Checkmate In One Move(Tricky!)
(WHITE TO MOVE)

Diagram 1

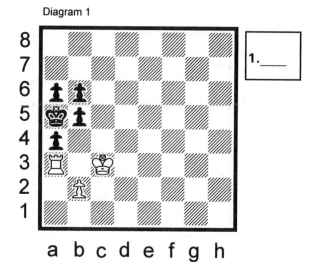

1.____

Diagram 2

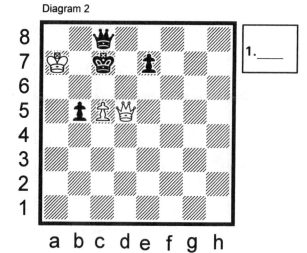

1.____

Diagram 3

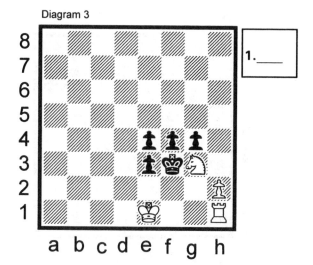

1.____

Diagram 4

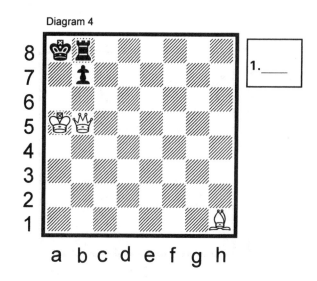

1.____

Diagram 5

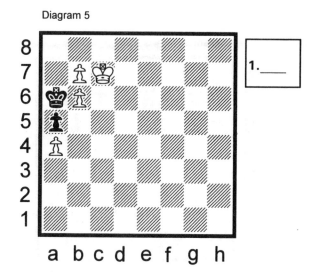

1.____

Diagram 6

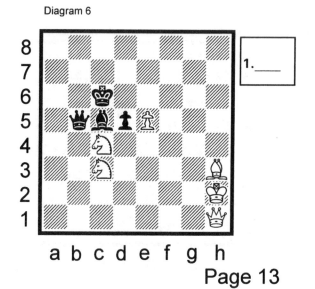

1.____

Winning Material
(WHITE TO MOVE)

Diagram 1

Diagram 2

Diagram 3

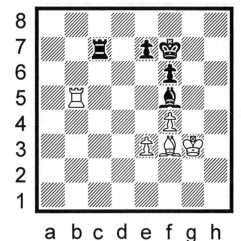

Diagram 4

Diagram 5

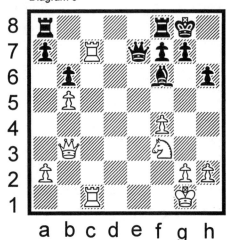

Diagram 6

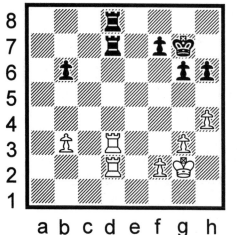

Basic Tactics--Using The Pin
(WHITE TO MOVE)

Diagram 1

Diagram 2

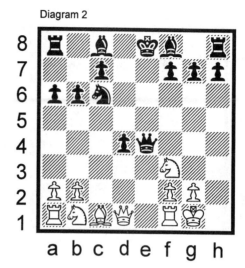

Diagram 3

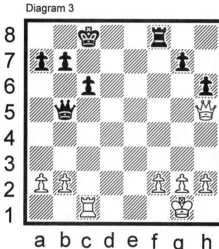

Diagram 4

Diagram 5

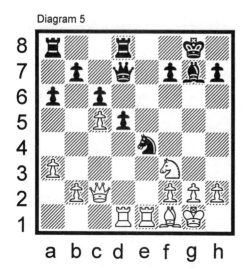

Diagram 6

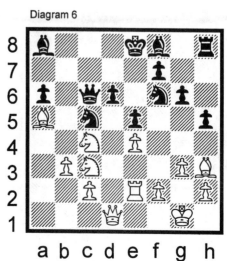

Basic Tactics--The Pin

(WHITE TO MOVE)

Diagram 1

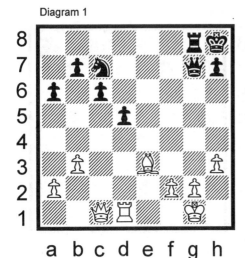

Diagram 2

Diagram 3

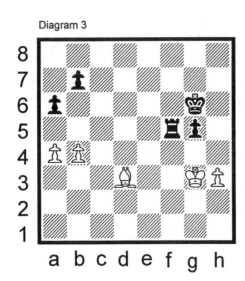

Diagram 4

Diagram 5

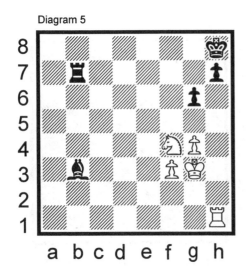

Diagram 6

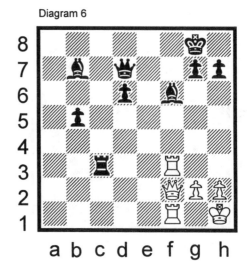

Basic Tactics--Attacking Pinned Pieces
(WHITE TO MOVE)

Diagram 1

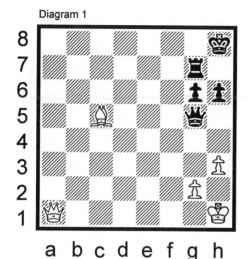

Diagram 2

Diagram 3

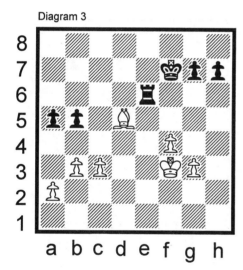

Diagram 4

Diagram 5

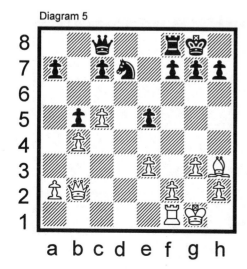

Diagram 6

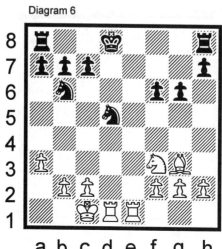

Basic Tactics--Attacking Pinned Pieces
(WHITE TO MOVE)

Diagram 1

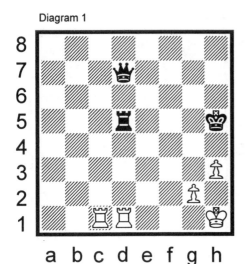

Diagram 2

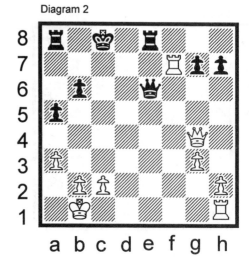

Diagram 3

Diagram 4

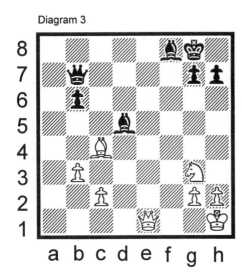

Diagram 5

Diagram 6

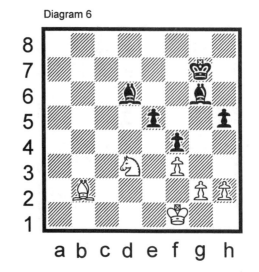

Winning Material-Trapped Pieces
(WHITE TO MOVE)

Diagram 1

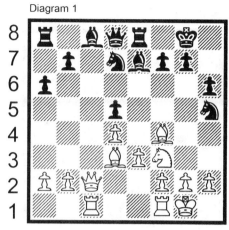

Diagram 2

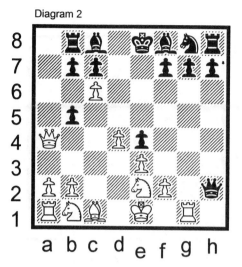

Diagram 3

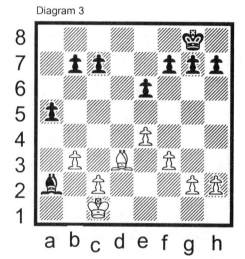

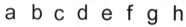

Diagram 4

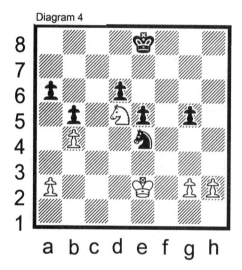

Diagram 5

Diagram 6

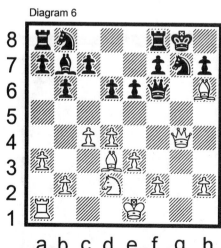

Double Attack With The Queen
(WHITE TO MOVE)

Diagram 1

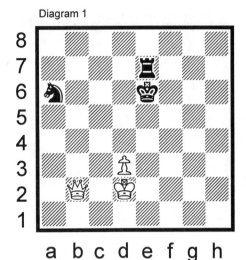

Diagram 2

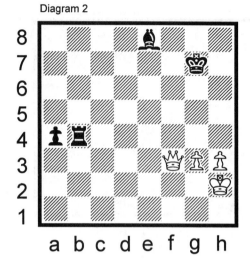

Diagram 3

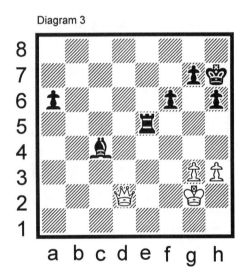

Diagram 4

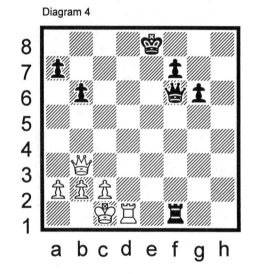

Diagram 5

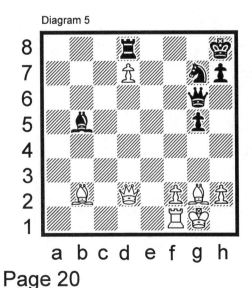

Diagram 6

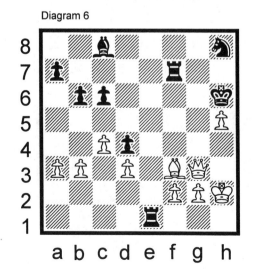

Page 20

Double Attack With The Queen
(WHITE TO MOVE)

Diagram 1

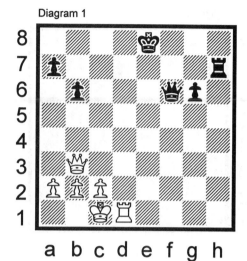

Diagram 2

Diagram 3

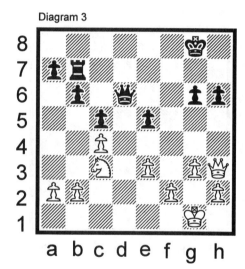

Diagram 4

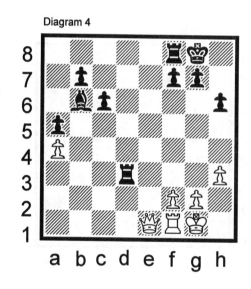

Diagram 5

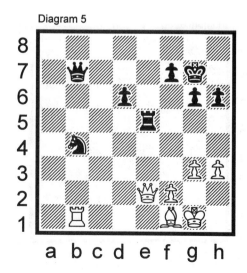

Diagram 6

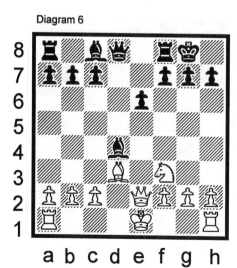

Double Attacks With the Knight
(WHITE TO MOVE)

Diagram 1

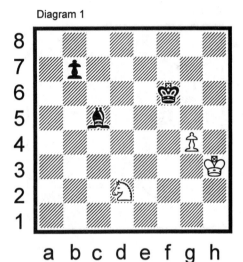

Diagram 2

Diagram 3

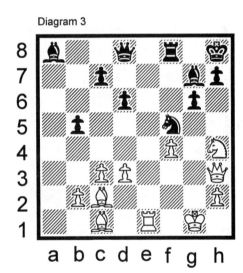

Diagram 4

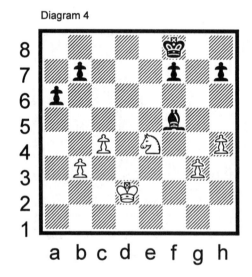

Diagram 5

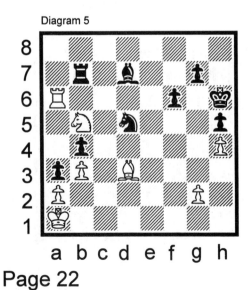

Diagram 6

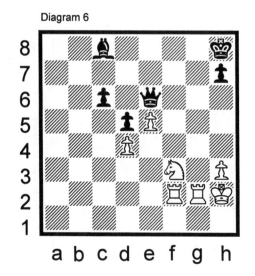

Page 22

Double Attacks With Rooks and Bishops
(WHITE TO MOVE)

Diagram 1

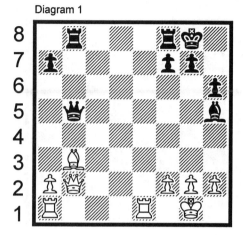

Diagram 2

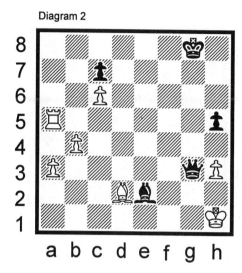

Diagram 3

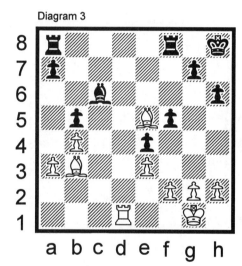

Diagram 4

Diagram 5

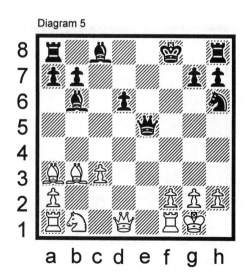

Diagram 6

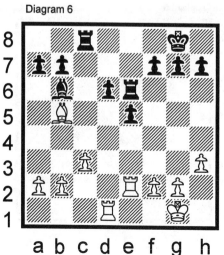

Double Attacks With Pawns and Kings
(WHITE TO MOVE)

Diagram 1

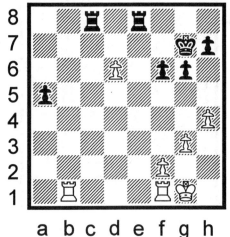

Diagram 2

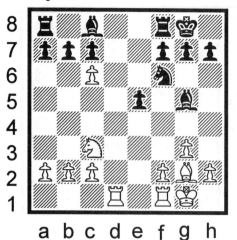

Diagram 3

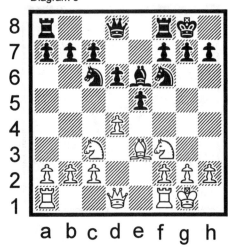

Diagram 4

Diagram 5

Diagram 6

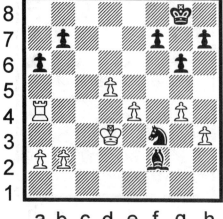

Basic Tactics--Discovered Attacks and Double Check
(WHITE TO MOVE)

Diagram 1

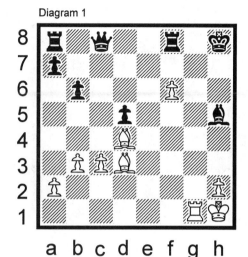

Diagram 2

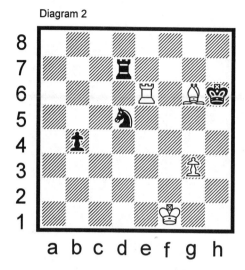

Diagram 3

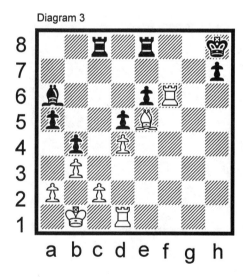

Diagram 4

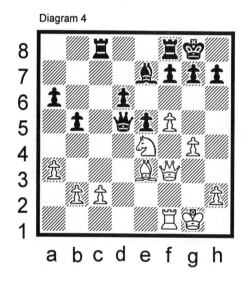

Diagram 5

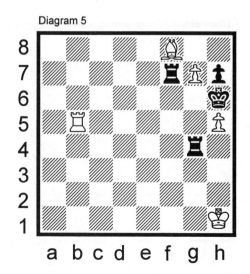

Diagram 6

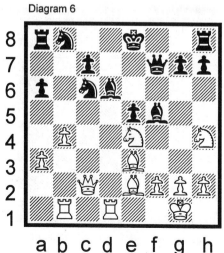

Basic Tactics--Discovered Attacks & Double Checks
(WHITE TO MOVE)

Diagram 1

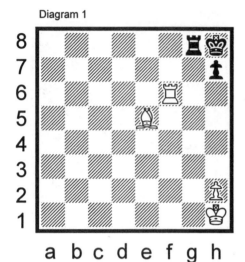

Diagram 2

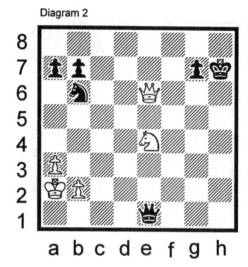

Diagram 3

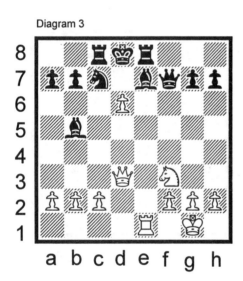

Diagram 4

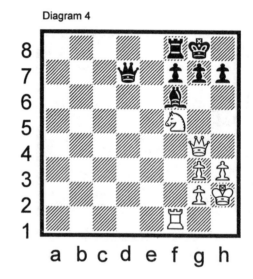

Diagram 5

Diagram 6

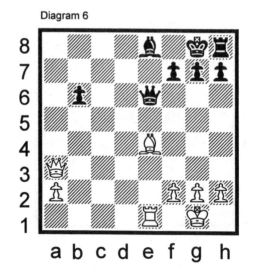

Basic Tactics--The Skewer
(WHITE TO MOVE)

Diagram 1

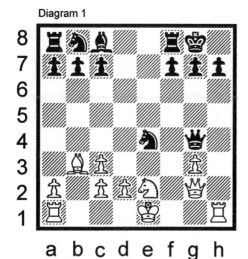

Diagram 2

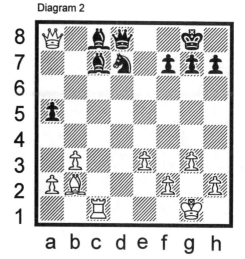

Diagram 3

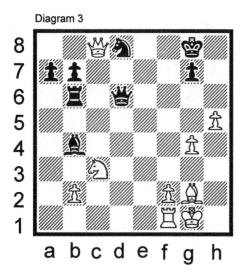

Diagram 4

Diagram 5

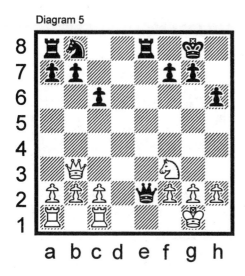

Diagram 6

Basic Tactics--The Skewer
(WHITE TO MOVE)

Diagram 1

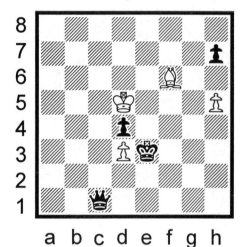

Diagram 2

Diagram 3

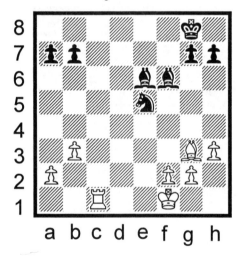

Diagram 4

Diagram 5

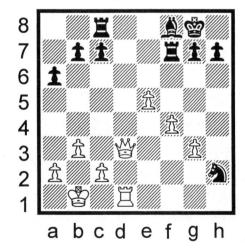

Diagram 6

Discovered Attacks and Double Check
(WHITE TO MOVE)

Diagram 1

Diagram 2

Diagram 3

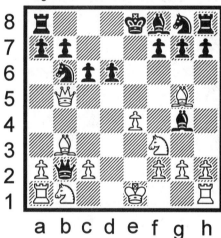

Diagram 4

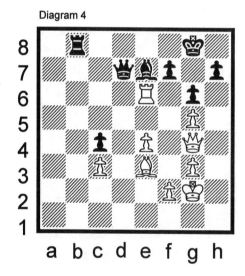

Diagram 5

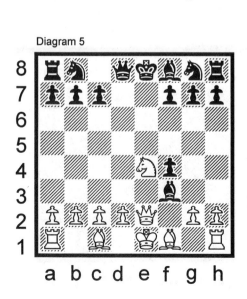

Diagram 6

Page 29

Tactics II--Discovered Attacks & Double Checks
(WHITE TO MOVE)

Diagram 1

Diagram 2

Diagram 3

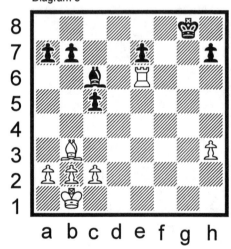

Diagram 4

Diagram 5

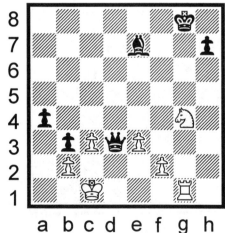

Diagram 6

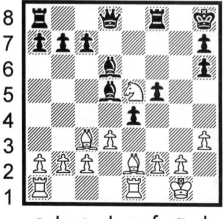

Tactics II—The Decoy
(White to Move)

Diagram 1

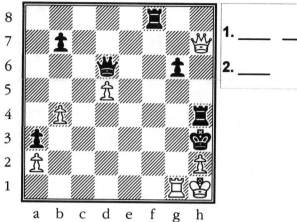

1. _____ _____

2. _____

Diagram 2

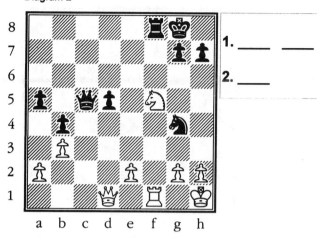

1. _____ _____

2. _____

Diagram 3

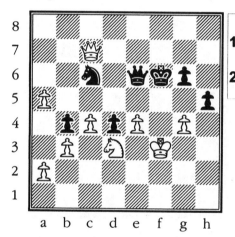

1. _____ _____

2. _____

Diagram 4

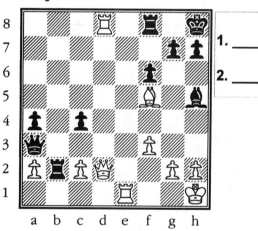

1. _____ _____

2. _____

Diagram 5

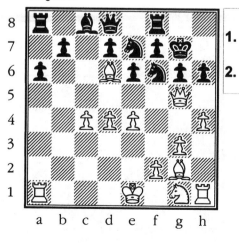

1. _____ _____

2. _____

Diagram 6

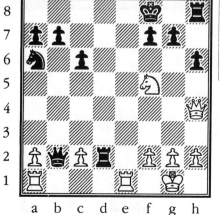

1. _____ _____

2. _____

Tactics II--The Pin
(WHITE TO MOVE)

Diagram 1

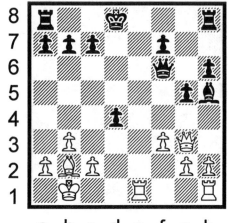

Diagram 2

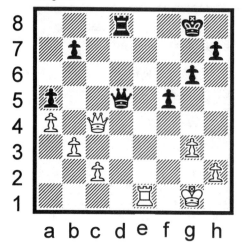

Diagram 3

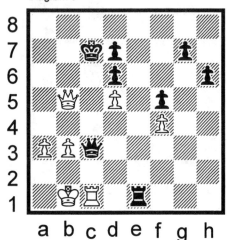

Diagram 4

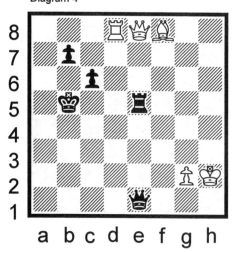

Diagram 5

Diagram 6

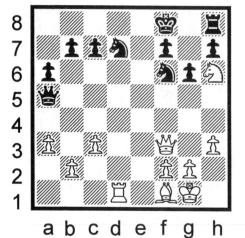

Tactics II--The Double Attack
(WHITE TO MOVE)

Diagram 1

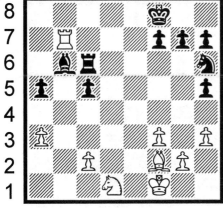

Diagram 2

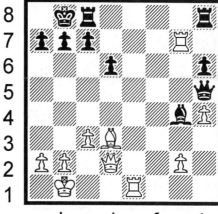

Diagram 3

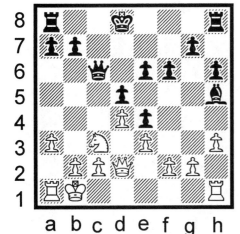

Diagram 4

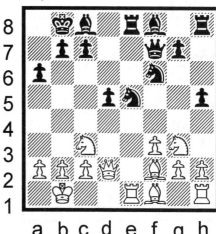

Diagram 5

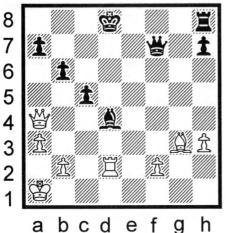

Diagram 6

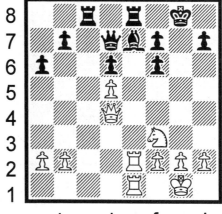

Basic Tactics--Double Attacks

(WHITE TO MOVE)

Diagram 1

Diagram 2

Diagram 3

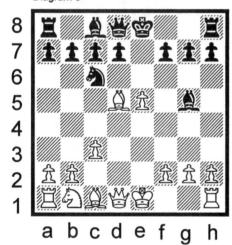

Diagram 4

Diagram 5

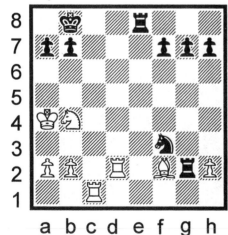

Diagram 6

Tactics II—Combination Quiz
(WHITE TO MOVE)

Diagram 1

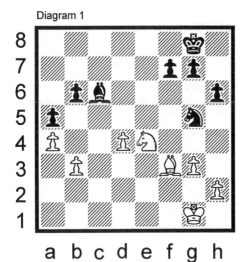

Diagram 2

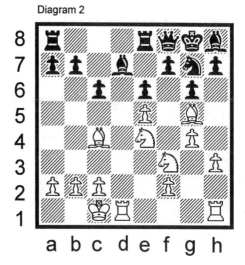

Diagram 3

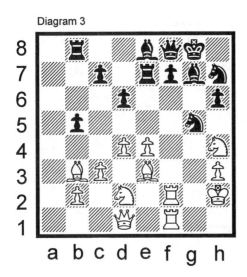

Diagram 4

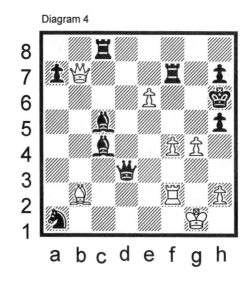

Diagram 5

Diagram 6

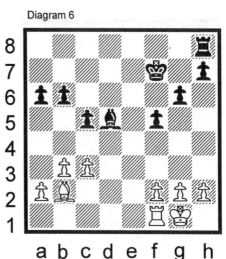

Tactics II--Advanced Techniques
(WHITE TO MOVE)

Diagram 1

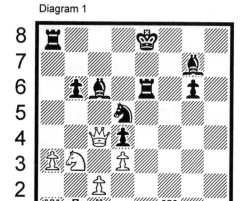

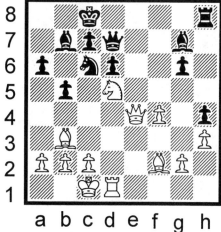

Diagram 2

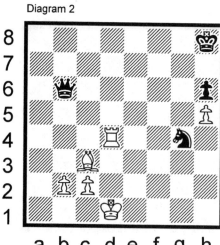

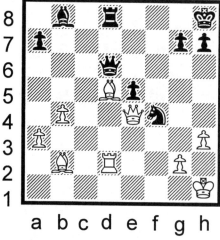

Diagram 3

Diagram 4

Diagram 5

Diagram 6

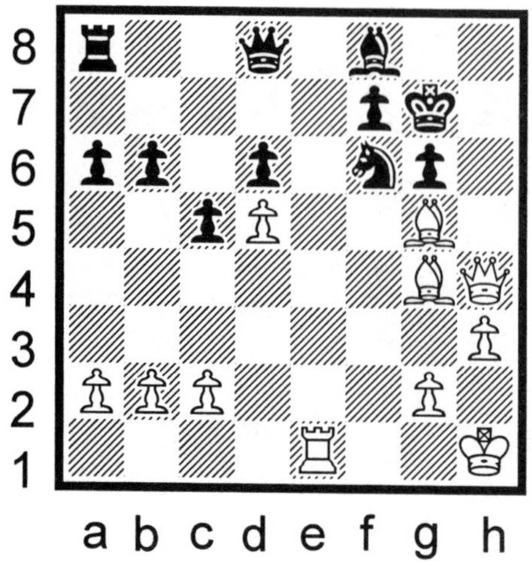

Tactics II—Advanced Combinations
(WHITE TO MOVE)

Diagram 1

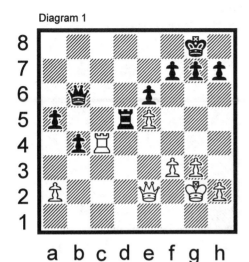

Diagram 2

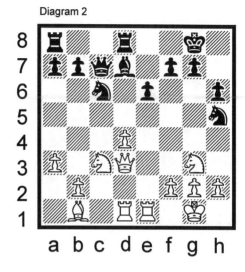

Diagram 3

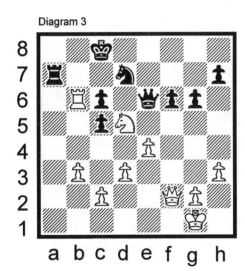

Diagram 4

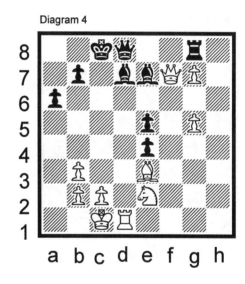

Diagram 5

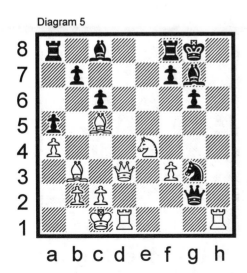

Diagram 6

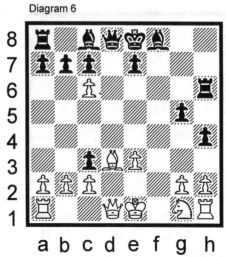

Tactics II--Advanced Combinations
(WHITE TO MOVE)

Diagram 1

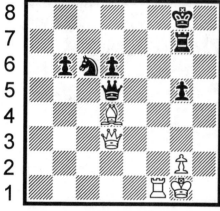

Diagram 2

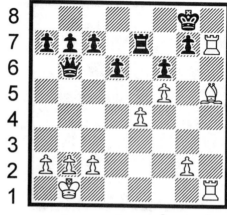

Diagram 3

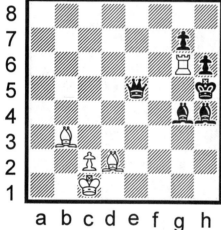

Diagram 4

Diagram 5

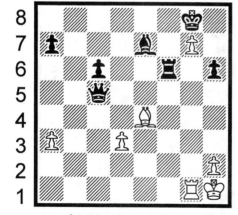

Diagram 6

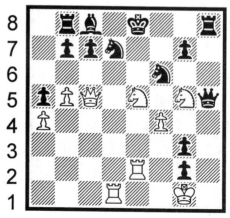

Tactics--Advanced Combinations
(WHITE TO MOVE)

Diagram 1

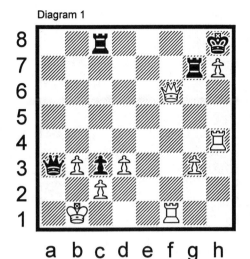

Diagram 2

Diagram 3

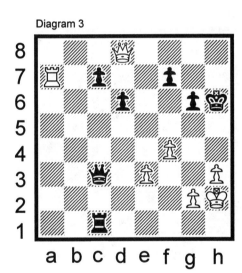

Diagram 4

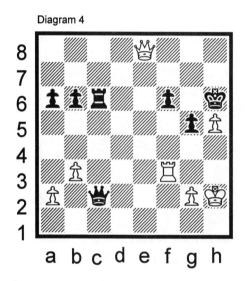

Diagram 5

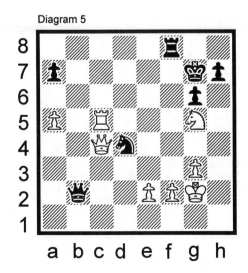

Diagram 6

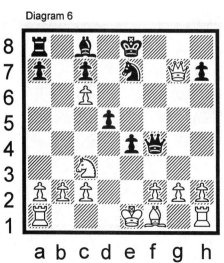

Tactics II--The Pawn Breakthrough
(WHITE TO MOVE)

Diagram 1

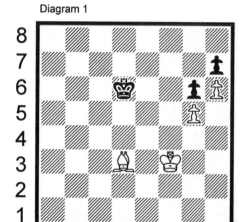

Diagram 2

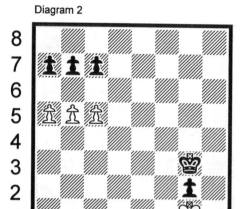

Diagram 3

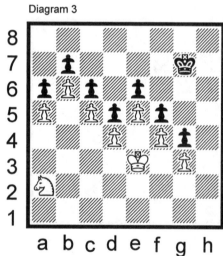

Diagram 4

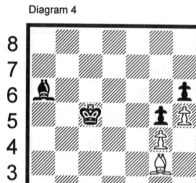

Diagram 5

Diagram 6

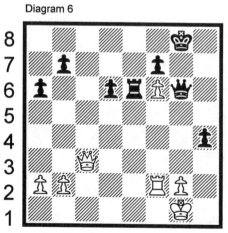

Tactics II—Advanced Combinations
(WHITE TO MOVE)

Diagram 1
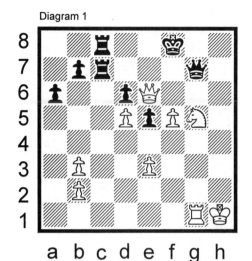

Diagram 2
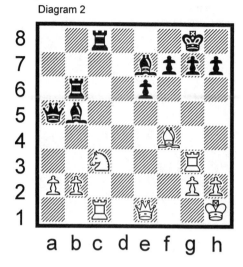

Diagram 3
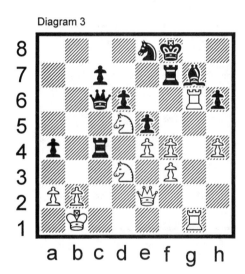

Diagram 4
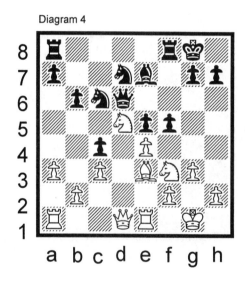

Diagram 5
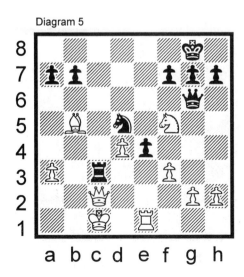

Diagram 6
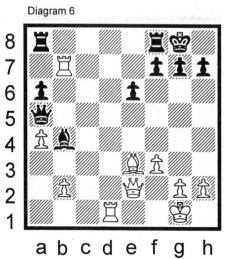

Tactics II--Double Attacks
(WHITE TO MOVE)

Diagram 1

Diagram 2

Diagram 3

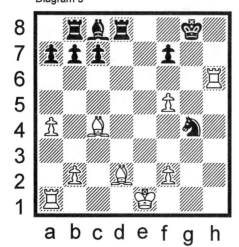

Diagram 4

Diagram 5

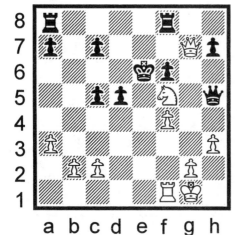

Diagram 6

Forced Mate In Two
(WHITE TO MOVE)

Diagram 1

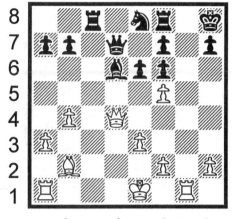

Diagram 2

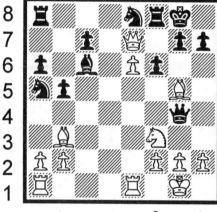

Diagram 3

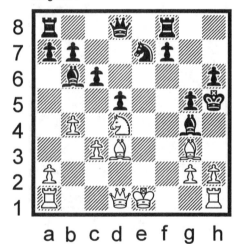

Diagram 4

Diagram 5

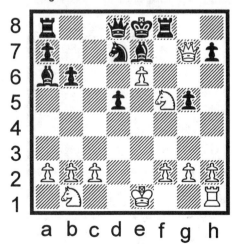

Diagram 6

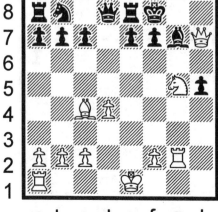

Mate in Two With Discovered and Double Check
(WHITE TO MOVE)

Diagram 1

Diagram 2

Diagram 3

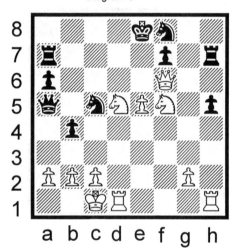

Diagram 4

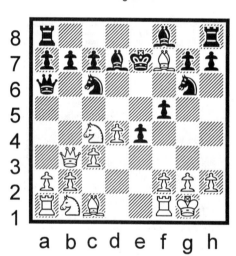

Diagram 5

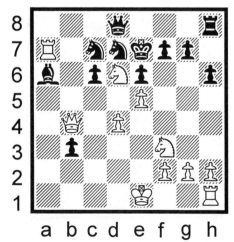

Diagram 6

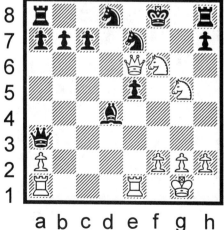

Mate in 2 w/Discovered Attacks & Double Check
(WHITE TO MOVE)

Diagram 1

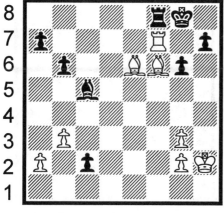

Diagram 2

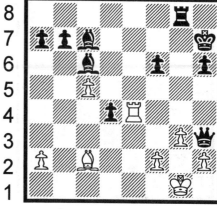

Diagram 3

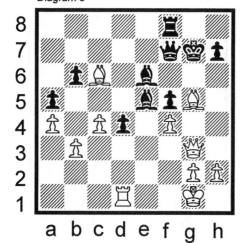

Diagram 4

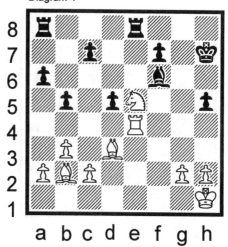

Diagram 5

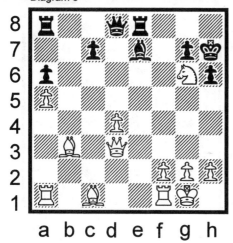

Diagram 6

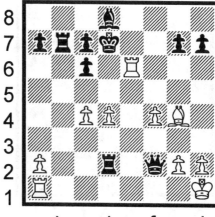

Page 45

Mate In 2 W/Discovered Attacks & Double Check
(WHITE TO MOVE)

Diagram 1

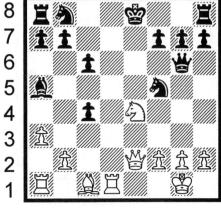

a b c d e f g h

Diagram 2

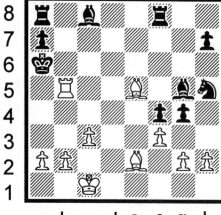

a b c d e f g h

Diagram 3

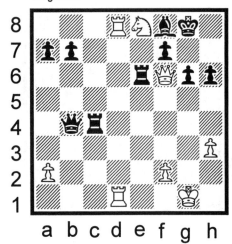

a b c d e f g h

Diagram 4

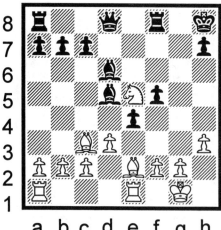

a b c d e f g h

Diagram 5

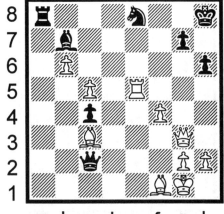

a b c d e f g h

Diagram 6

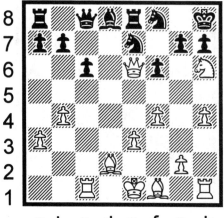

a b c d e f g h

Page 46

Mate In Two with Rooks & Minor Pieces
(WHITE TO MOVE)

Diagram 1

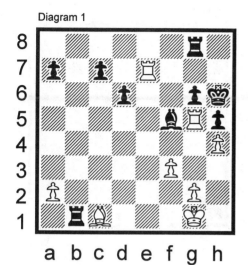

Diagram 2

Diagram 3

Diagram 4

Diagram 5

Diagram 6

Mostly Pawn Mates
(WHITE TO MOVE)

Diagram 1

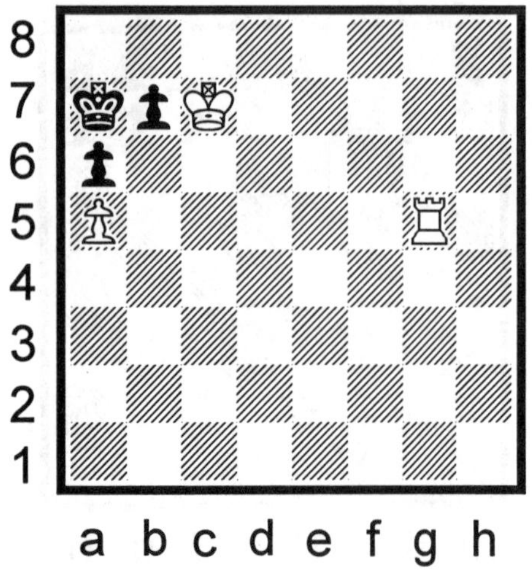

Diagram 2

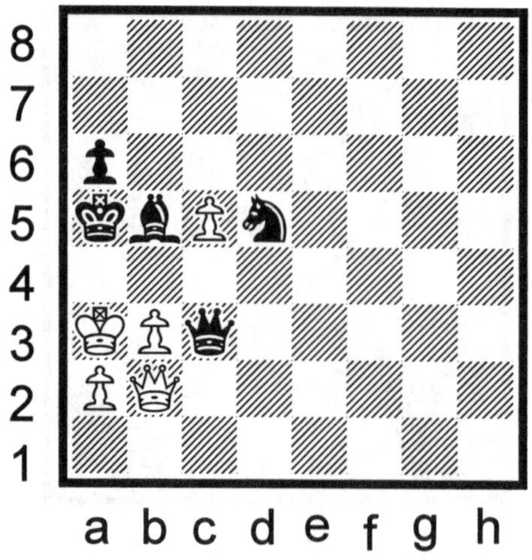

Diagram 3

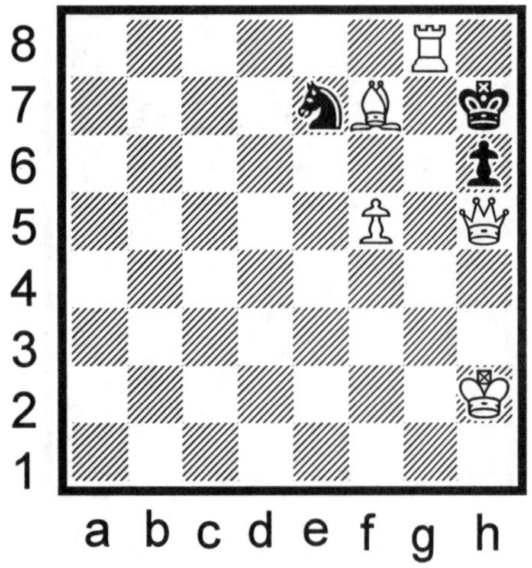

Diagram 4

Diagram 5

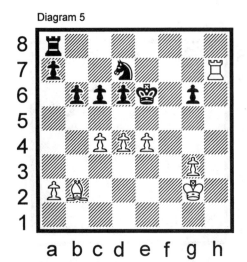

Diagram 6

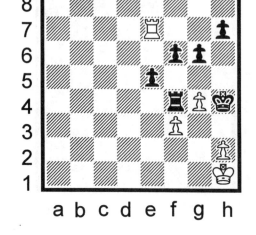

Mating Attacks on the Castled King
(WHITE TO MOVE)

Diagram 1

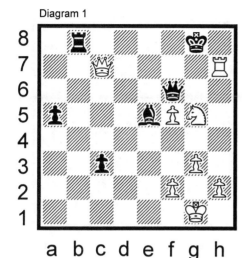

Diagram 2

Diagram 3

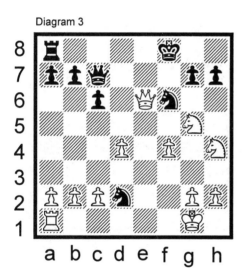

Diagram 4

Diagram 5

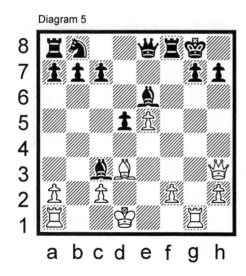

Diagram 6

Forced Mate In Two
(WHITE TO MOVE)

Diagram 1

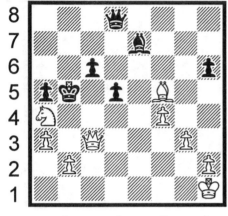

Diagram 2

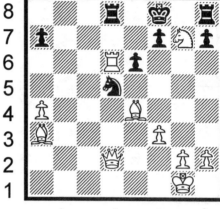

Diagram 3

Diagram 4

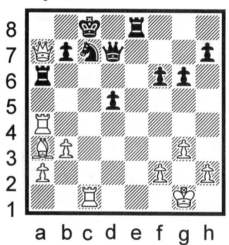

Diagram 5

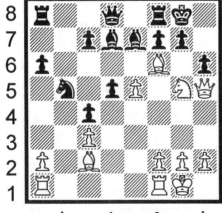

Diagram 6

Forced Mate In Two
(White to Move)

Diagram 1

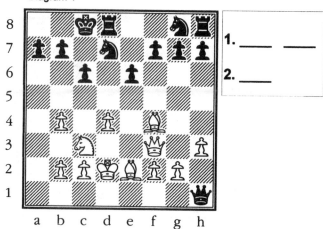

1. ____ ____

2. ____

Diagram 2

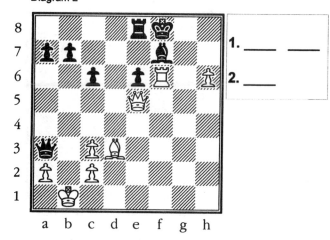

1. ____ ____

2. ____

Diagram 3

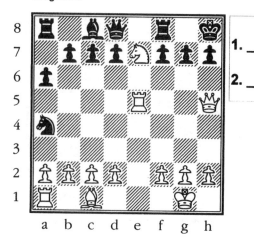

1. ____ ____

2. ____

Diagram 4

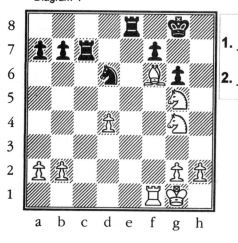

1. ____ ____

2. ____

Diagram 5

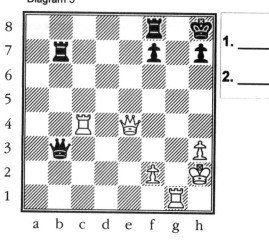

1. ____ ____

2. ____

Diagram 6

1. ____ ____

2. ____

Forced Mate In Two
(WHITE TO MOVE)

Diagram 1

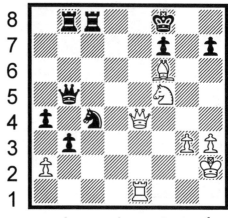
Diagram 2

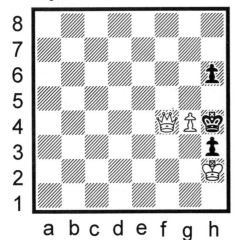
Diagram 3

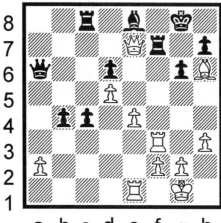
Diagram 4

Diagram 5

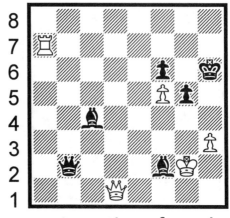
Diagram 6

Forced Mate In Two
(WHITE TO MOVE)

Diagram 1
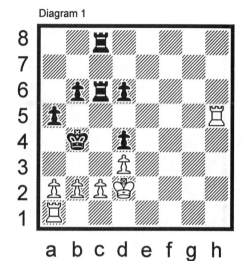

Diagram 2
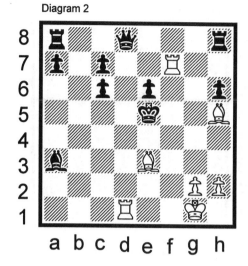

Diagram 3
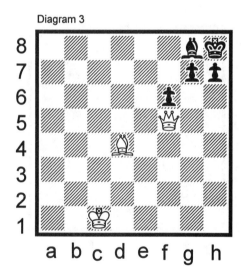

Diagram 4
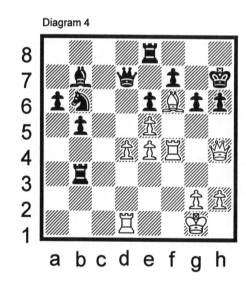

Diagram 5
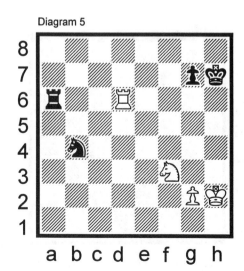

Diagram 6
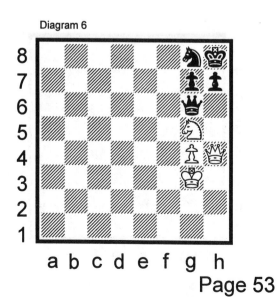

Forced Mate In Two
(WHITE TO MOVE)

Diagram 1

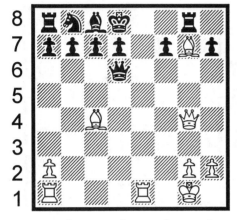

Diagram 2

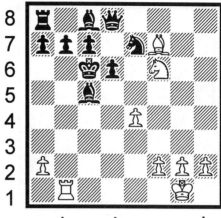

Diagram 3

Diagram 4

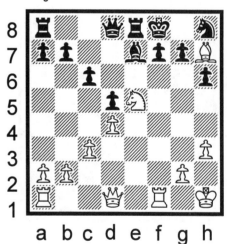

Diagram 5

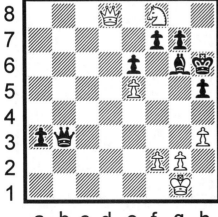

Diagram 6

Forced Mate In Two
(WHITE TO MOVE)

Diagram 1

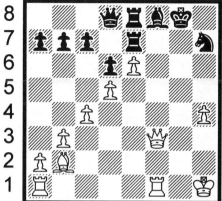

1.____ ____

2.____

Diagram 2

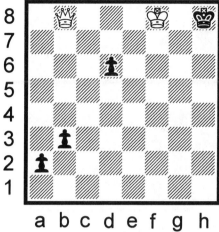

1.____ ____

2.____

Diagram 3

1.____ ____

2.____

Diagram 4

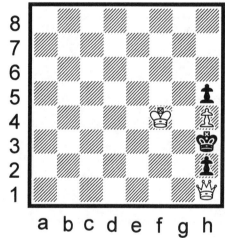

1.____ ____

2.____

Diagram 5

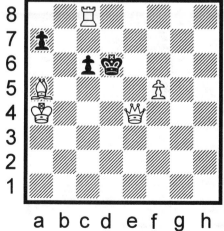

1.____ ____

2.____

Diagram 6

1.____ ____

2.____

Forced Mate In Two
(WHITE TO MOVE)

Diagram 1

Diagram 2

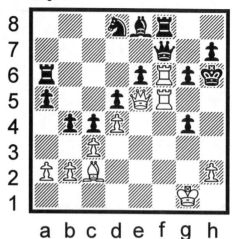

Diagram 3

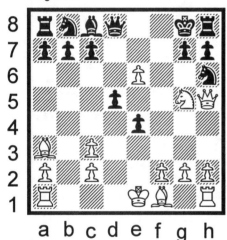

Diagram 4

Diagram 5

Diagram 6

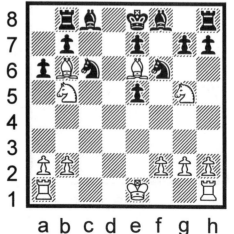

Forced Mate In Two
(White to Move)

Diagram 1

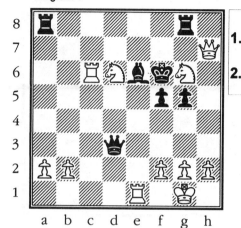

1. ____ ____

2. ____

Diagram 2

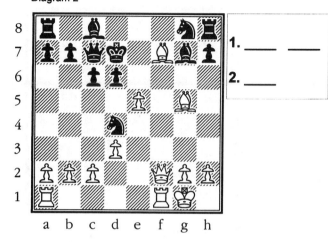

1. ____ ____

2. ____

Diagram 3

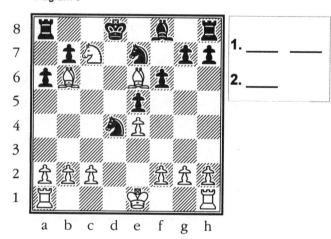

1. ____ ____

2. ____

Diagram 4

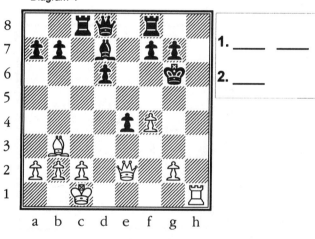

1. ____ ____

2. ____

Diagram 5

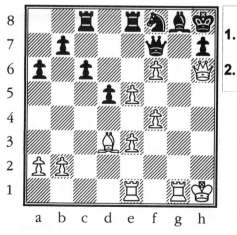

1. ____ ____

2. ____

Diagram 6

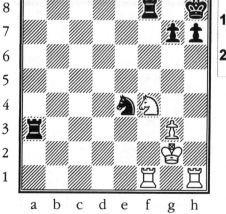

1. ____ ____

2. ____

Forced Mate In Two
(WHITE TO MOVE)

Diagram 1

Diagram 2

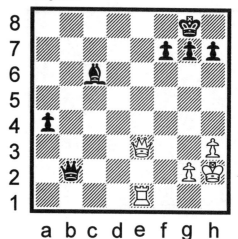

Diagram 3

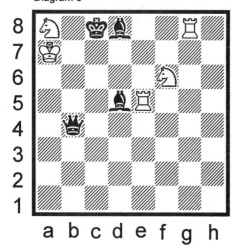

Diagram 4

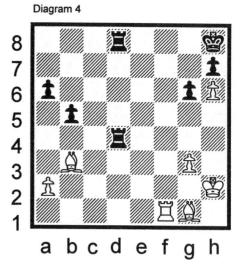

Diagram 5

Diagram 6

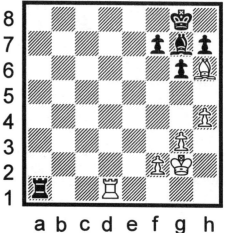

Forced Mate In Two
(WHITE TO MOVE)

Diagram 1

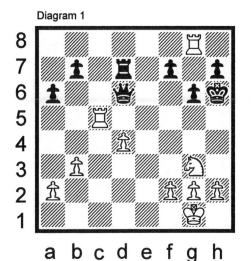

Diagram 2

Diagram 3

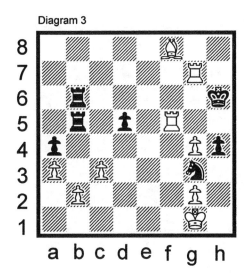

Diagram 4

Diagram 5

Diagram 6

Page 59

Forced Mate with Deflection
(WHITE TO MOVE)

Diagram 1

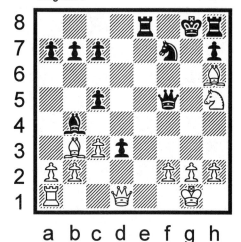

Diagram 2

Diagram 3

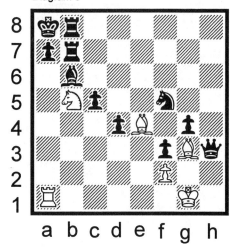

Diagram 4

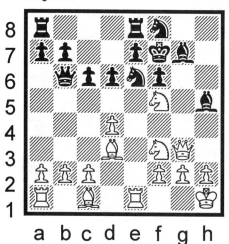

Diagram 5

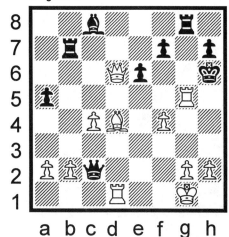

Diagram 6

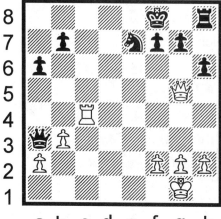

Forced Mate In Two
(White to Move)

Diagram 1

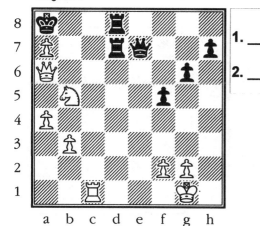

1. ____ ____

2. ____

Diagram 2

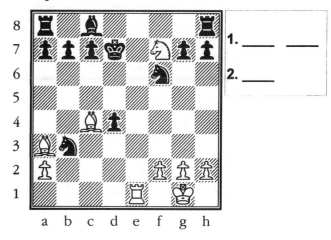

1. ____ ____

2. ____

Diagram 3

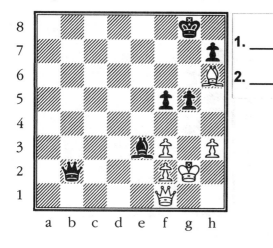

1. ____ ____

2. ____

Diagram 4

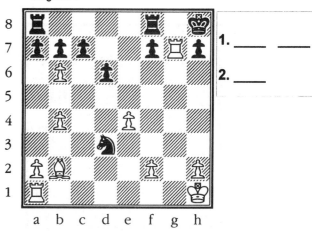

1. ____ ____

2. ____

Diagram 5

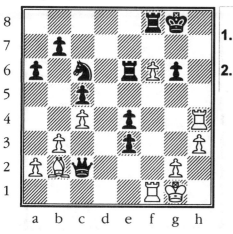

1. ____ ____

2. ____

Diagram 6

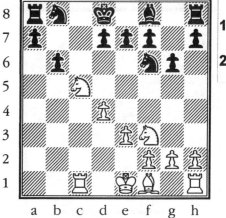

1. ____ ____

2. ____

Forced Mate In Two
(WHITE TO MOVE)

Diagram 1

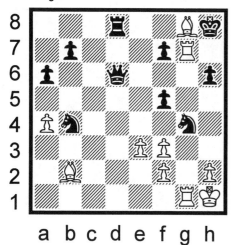

Diagram 2

Diagram 3

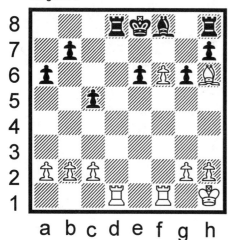

Diagram 4

Diagram 5

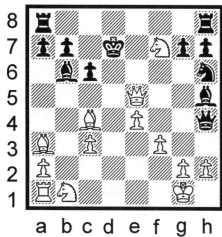

Diagram 6

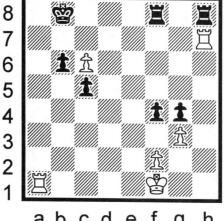

Forced Mate In Two
(WHITE TO MOVE)

Diagram 1

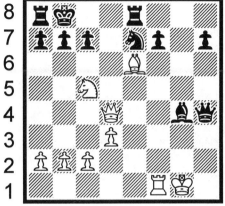

Diagram 2

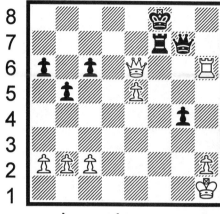

Diagram 3

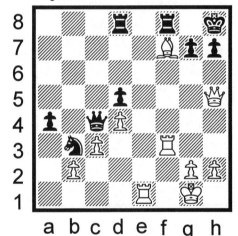

Diagram 4

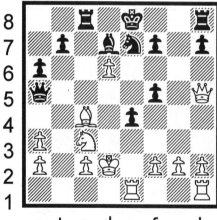

Diagram 5

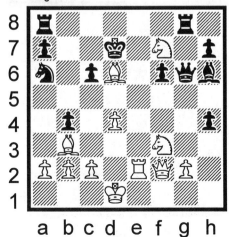

Diagram 6

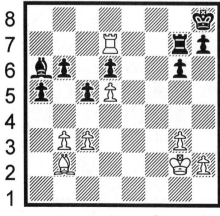

Forced Mate In Two
(WHITE TO MOVE)

Diagram 1

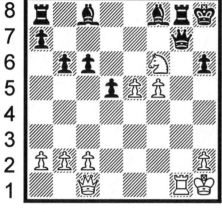

Diagram 2

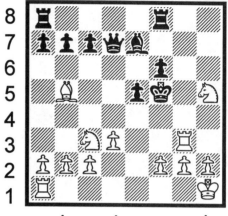

Diagram 3

Diagram 4

Diagram 5

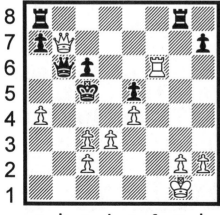

Diagram 6

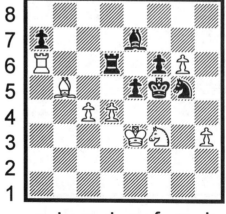

Forced Mate In Two
(WHITE TO MOVE)

Diagram 1

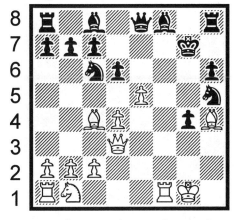

Diagram 2

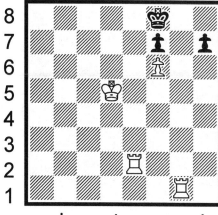

Diagram 3

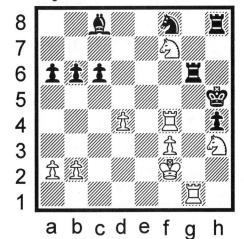

Diagram 4

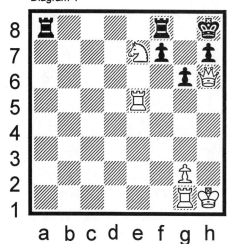

Diagram 5

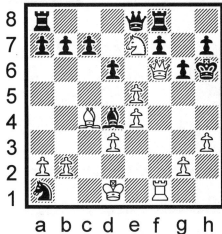

Diagram 6

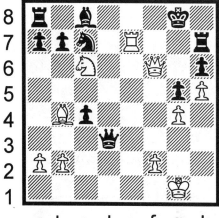

Forced Mate In Two
(WHITE TO MOVE)

Diagram 1

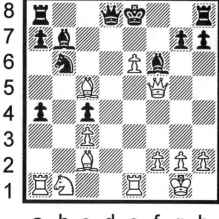

Diagram 2

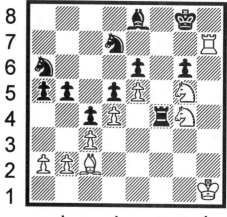

Diagram 3

Diagram 4

Diagram 5

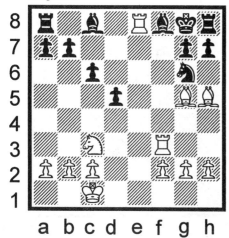

Diagram 6

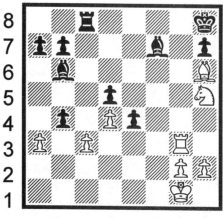

Forced Mate In Two

(WHITE TO MOVE)

Diagram 1

Diagram 2

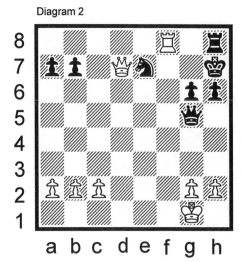

Diagram 3

Diagram 4

Diagram 5

Diagram 6

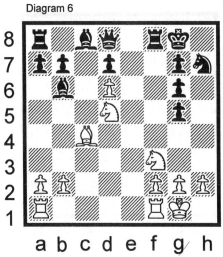

Forced Mate In Two
(WHITE TO MOVE)

Diagram 1

Diagram 2

Diagram 3

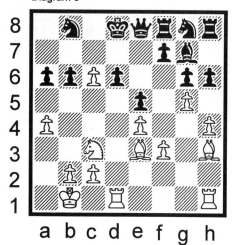

Diagram 4

Diagram 5

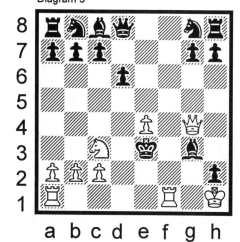

Diagram 6

Forced Mate In Two
(WHITE TO MOVE)

Diagram 1

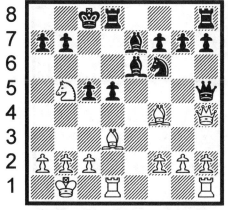

1.____ ____

2.____

Diagram 2

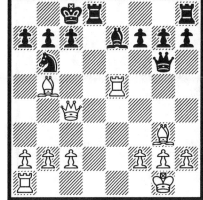

1.____ ____

2.____

Diagram 3

1.____ ____

2.____

Diagram 4

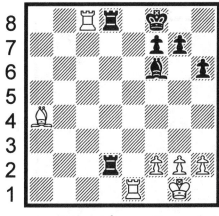

1.____ ____

2.____

Diagram 5

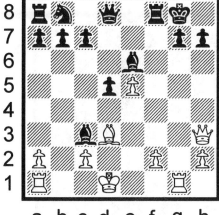

1.____ ____

2.____

Diagram 6

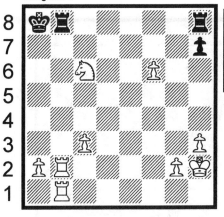

1.____ ____

2.____

Forced Mate In Two
(WHITE TO MOVE)

Diagram 1

Diagram 2

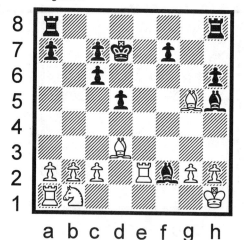

Diagram 3

Diagram 4

Diagram 5

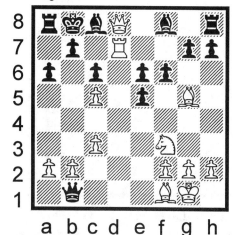

Diagram 6

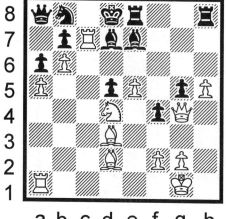

Forced Mate In Two
(WHITE TO MOVE)

Diagram 1

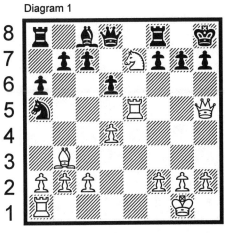

Diagram 2

Diagram 3

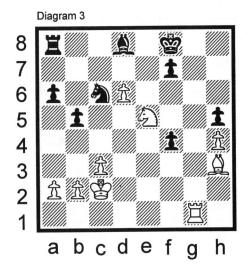

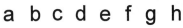

Diagram 4

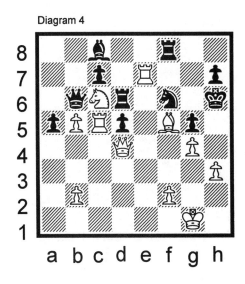

Diagram 5

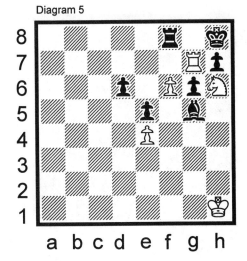

Diagram 6

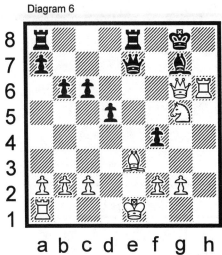

Forced Mate In Two
(WHITE TO MOVE)

Diagram 1

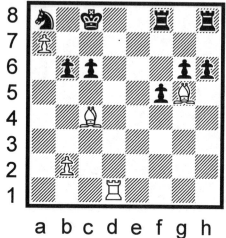

Diagram 2

Diagram 3

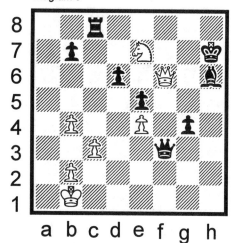

Diagram 4

Diagram 5

Diagram 6

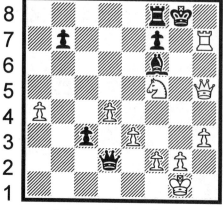

Forced Mate In Two
(WHITE TO MOVE)

Diagram 1

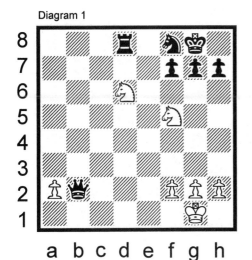

Diagram 2

Diagram 3

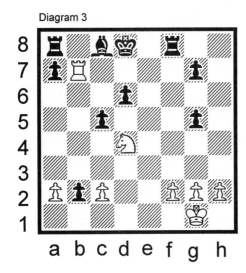

Diagram 4

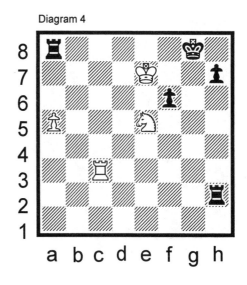

Diagram 5

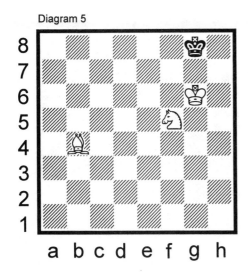

Diagram 6

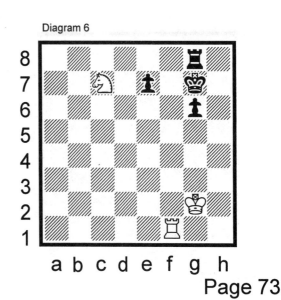

Forced Mate In Two

(WHITE TO MOVE)

Diagram 1

Diagram 2

Diagram 3

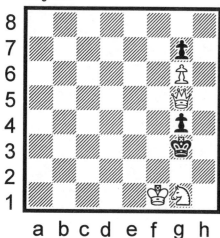

Diagram 4

Diagram 5

Diagram 6

Forced Mate In Two
(WHITE TO MOVE)

Diagram 1

Diagram 2

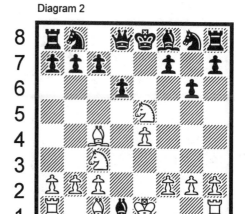

Diagram 3

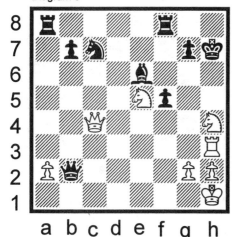

Diagram 4

Diagram 5

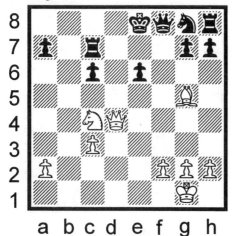

Diagram 6

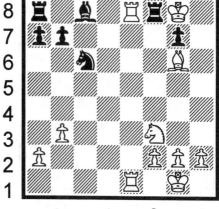

Forced Mate In Two
(WHITE TO MOVE)

Diagram 1

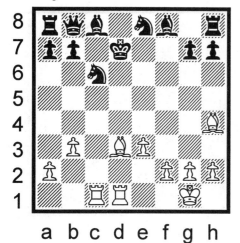

Diagram 2

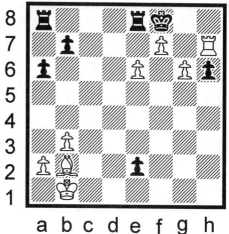

Diagram 3

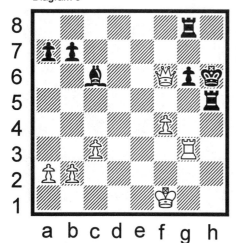

Diagram 4

Diagram 5

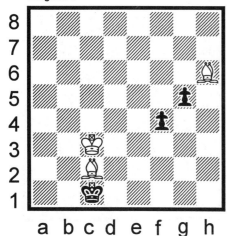

Diagram 6

Forced Mate In Two
(WHITE TO MOVE)

Diagram 1

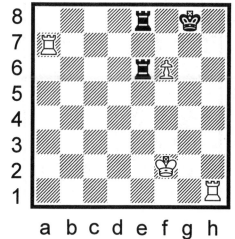

Diagram 2

Diagram 3

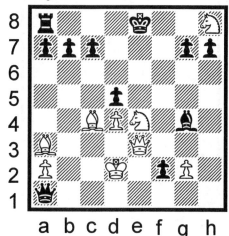

Diagram 4

Diagram 5

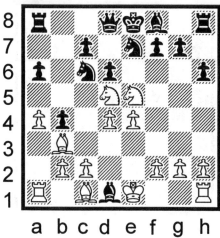

Diagram 6

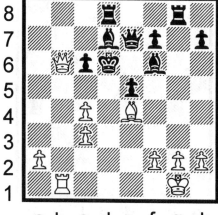

Forced Mate In Two
(WHITE TO MOVE)

Diagram 1

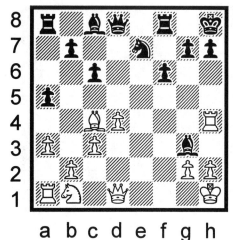

Diagram 2

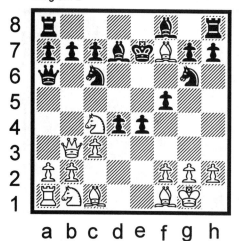

Diagram 3

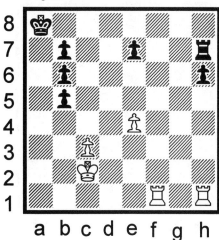

Diagram 4

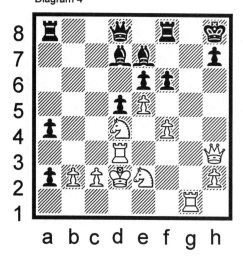

Diagram 5

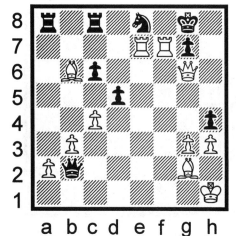

Diagram 6

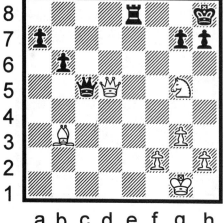

Forced Mate In Two
(WHITE TO MOVE)

Diagram 1

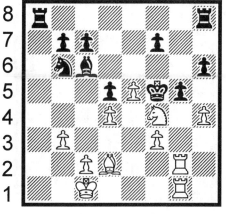

Diagram 2

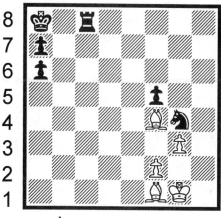

Diagram 3

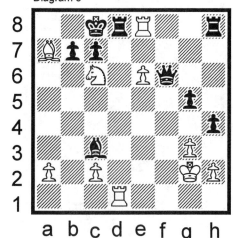

Diagram 4

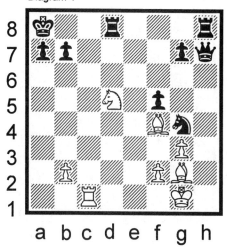

Diagram 5

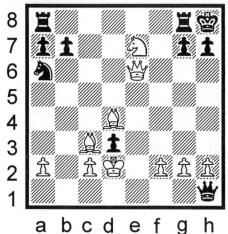

Diagram 6

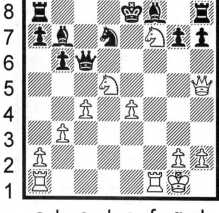

Mult-Option Forced Mate In Two
(WHITE TO MOVE)

Diagram 1

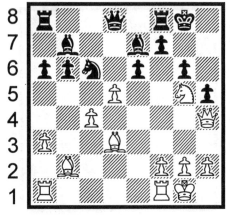

Diagram 2

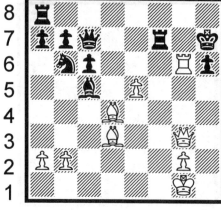

Diagram 3

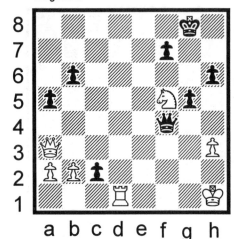

Diagram 4

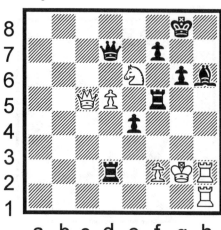

Diagram 5

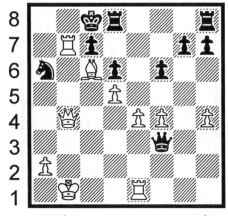

Diagram 6

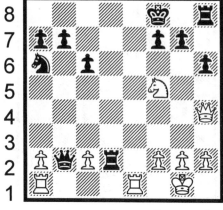

Multi-Option Forced Mate In Two
(WHITE TO MOVE)

Diagram 1

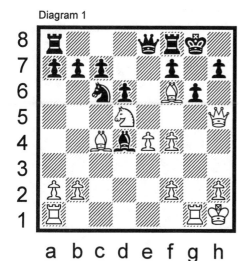

Diagram 2

Diagram 3

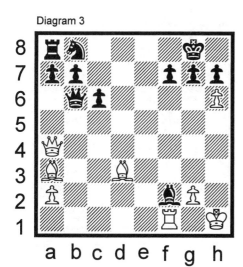

Diagram 4

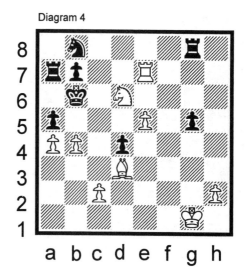

Diagram 5

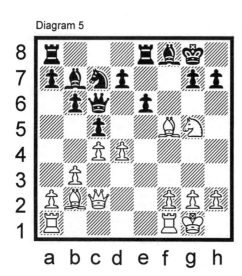

Diagram 6

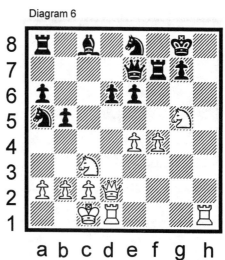

Multi-Option Forced Mate In Two
(WHITE TO MOVE)

Diagram 1

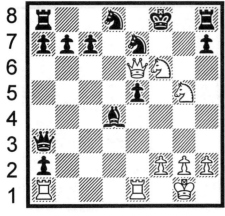

Diagram 2

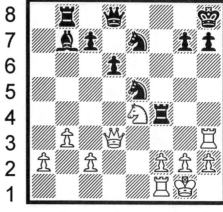

Diagram 3

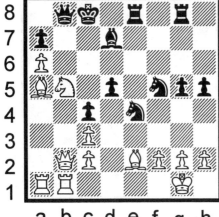

Diagram 4

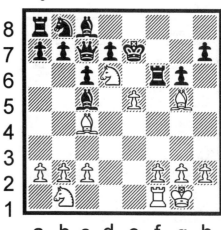

Diagram 5

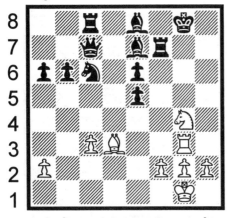

Diagram 6

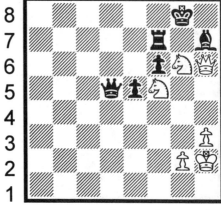

Forced Mate In Two
(WHITE TO MOVE)

Diagram 1

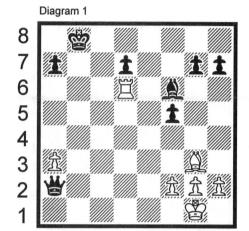

Diagram 2

Diagram 3

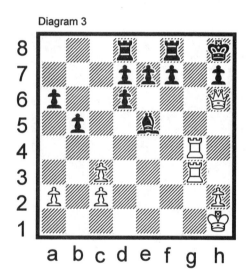

Diagram 4

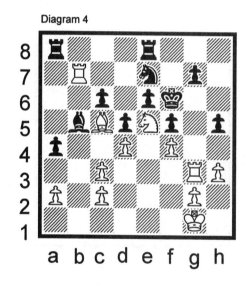

Diagram 5

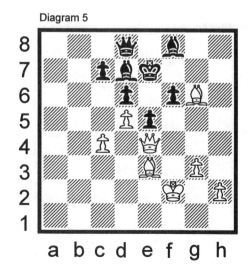

Diagram 6

Multi-Option Forced Mate In Two
(WHITE TO MOVE)

Diagram 1

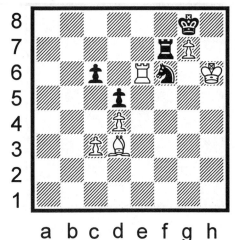

Diagram 2

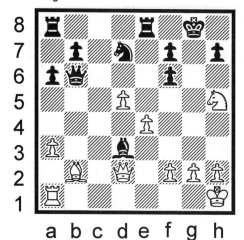

Diagram 3

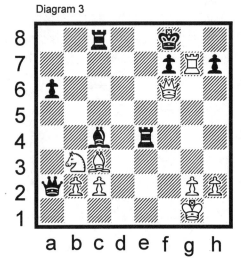

Diagram 4

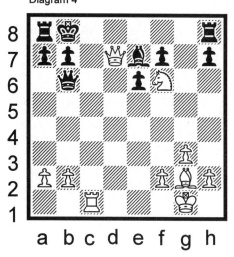

Diagram 5

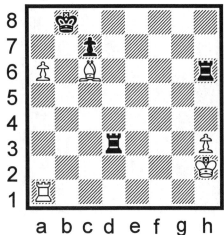

Diagram 6

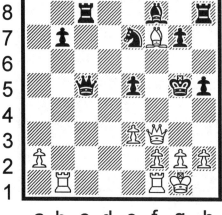

Multi-Option Forced Mate In Two
(WHITE TO MOVE)

Diagram 1

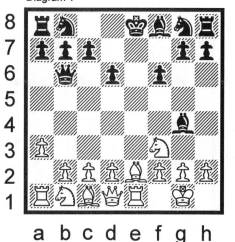

Diagram 2

Diagram 3

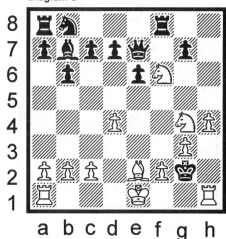

Diagram 4

Diagram 5

Diagram 6

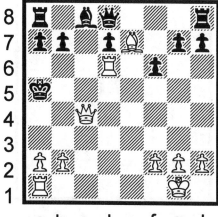

Multi-Option Forced Mate In Two
(WHITE TO MOVE)

Diagram 1

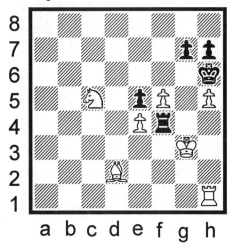

Diagram 2

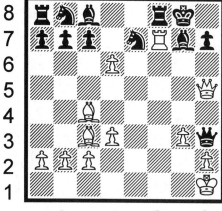

Diagram 3

Diagram 4

Diagram 5, Forced Mate In Two

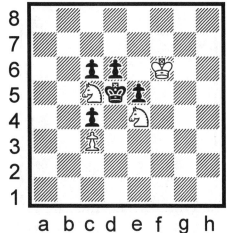

Diagram 6

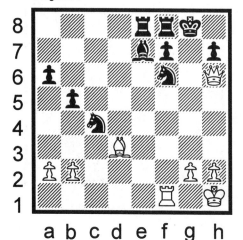

Multi-Option Forced Mate In Two

(WHITE TO MOVE)

Diagram 1

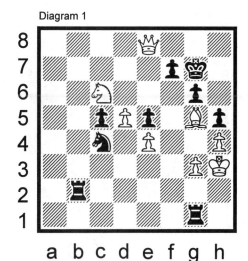

Diagram 2

Diagram 3

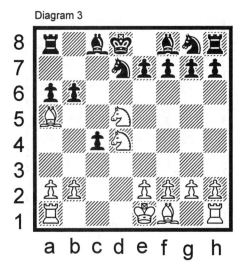

Diagram 4

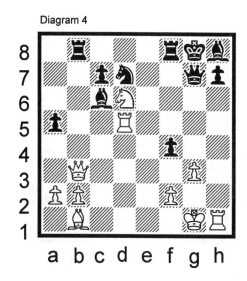

Diagram 5

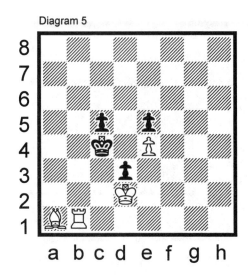

Diagram 6

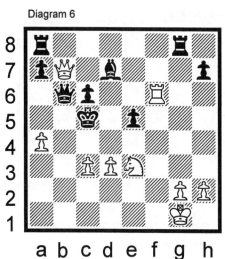

Multi-Option Forced Mate In Two
(WHITE TO MOVE)

Diagram 1

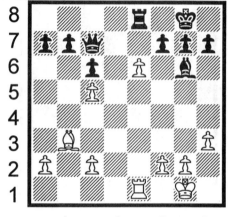

Diagram 2, Forced Mate in Two

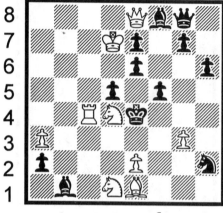

Diagram 3

Diagram 4

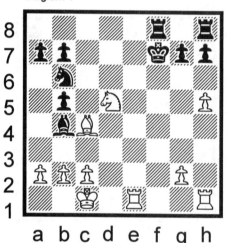

Diagram 5

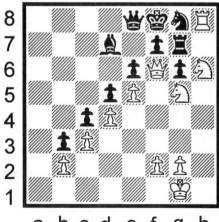

Diagram 6

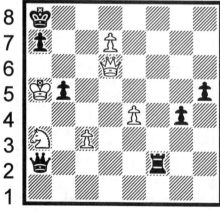

Multi-Optioned Forced Mate In Two
(WHITE TO MOVE)

Diagram 1

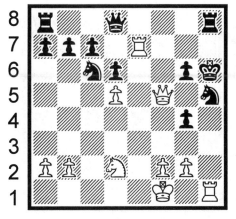

Diagram 2

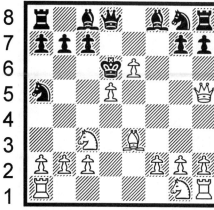

Diagram 3, Forced Mate In Two

Diagram 4

Diagram 5

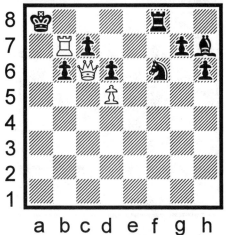

Diagram 6

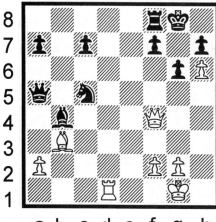

Italian Tactics
(WHITE TO MOVE)

Diagram 1

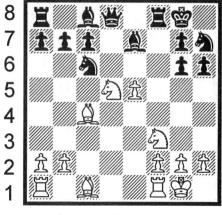

Diagram 2

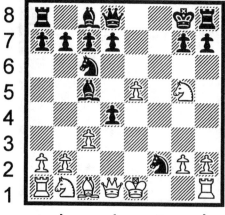

Diagram 3

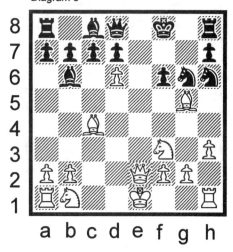

Diagram 4

Diagram 5

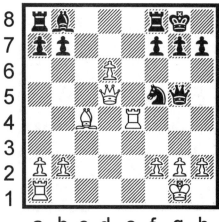

Diagram 6

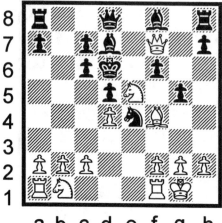

Italian Tactics
(WHITE TO MOVE)

Diagram 7

Diagram 8

Diagram 9

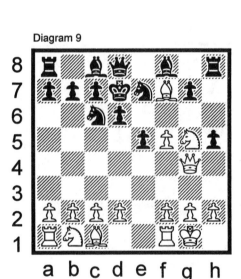

Diagram 10

Diagram 11

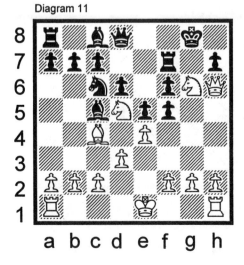

Diagram 12

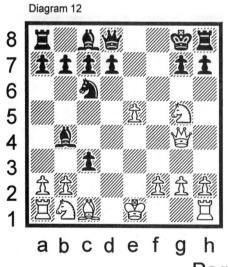

Italian Tactics
(WHITE TO MOVE)

Diagram 13

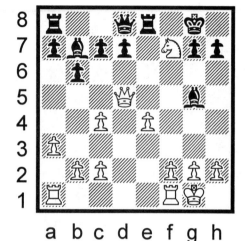

Diagram 14

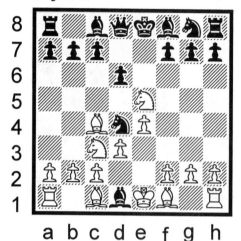

Diagram 15

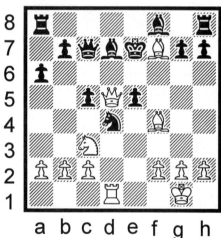

Diagram 16

Diagram 17

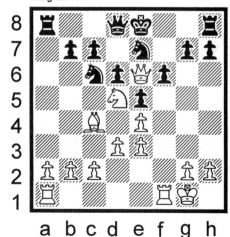

Diagram 18

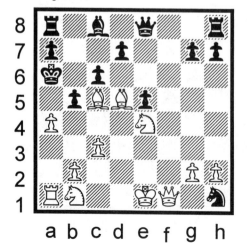

Italian Tactics
(WHITE TO MOVE)

Diagram 19

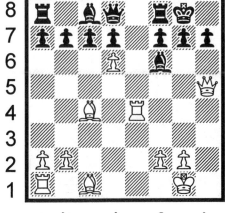

Diagram 20

Diagram 21

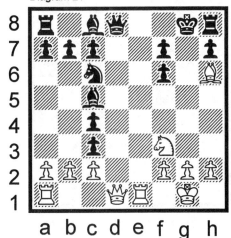

Diagram 22

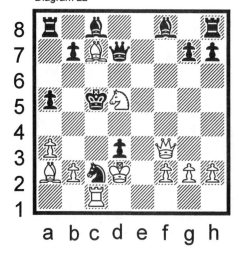

Diagram 23

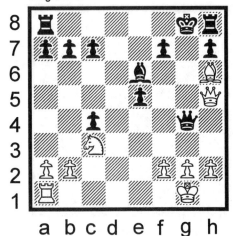

Diagram 24

Italian Tactics
(WHITE TO MOVE)

Diagram 25

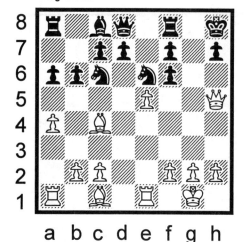

Diagram 26

Diagram 27

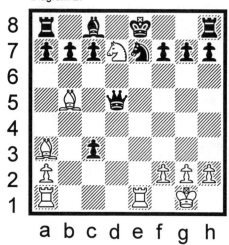

Diagram 28

Diagram 29

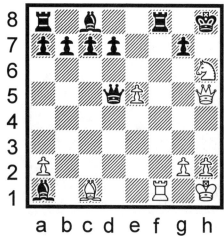

Diagram 30

Combination Quiz--Level II

(WHITE TO MOVE)

Diagram 1

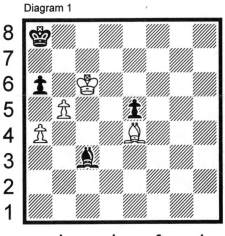

Diagram 2

Diagram 3

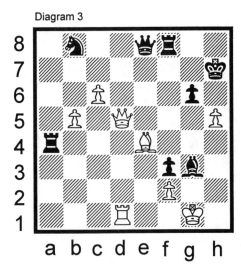

Diagram 4

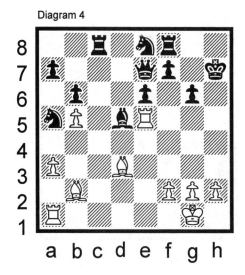

Diagram 5

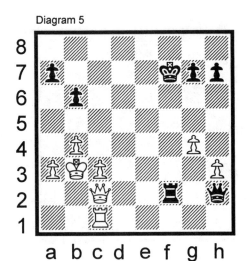

Diagram 6

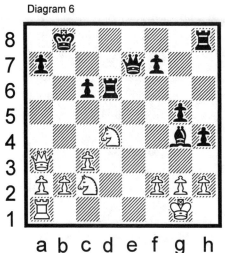

Combination Quiz--Level II
(WHITE TO MOVE)

Diagram 1

Diagram 2

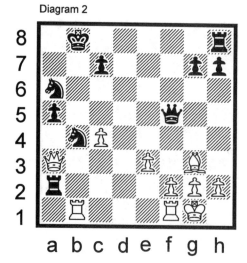

Diagram 3

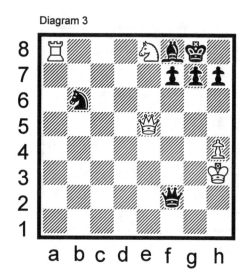

Diagram 4

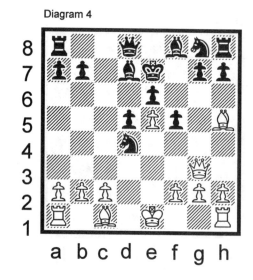

Diagram 5

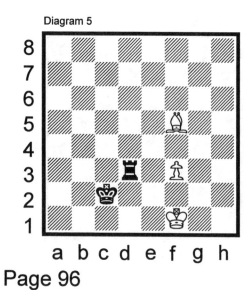

Diagram 6

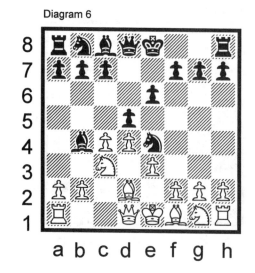

Combination Quiz--Level II
(WHITE TO MOVE)

Diagram 1

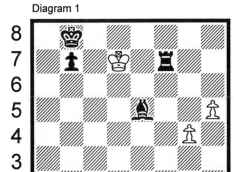

Diagram 2

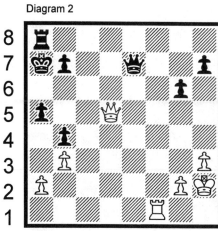

Diagram 3

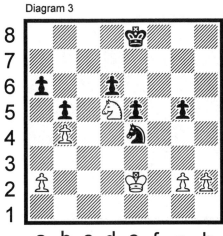

Diagram 4

Diagram 5

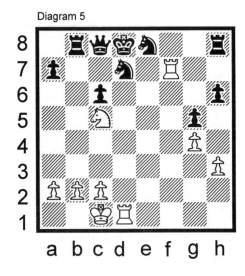

Diagram 6

Combination Quiz--Level II
(WHITE TO MOVE)

Diagram 1

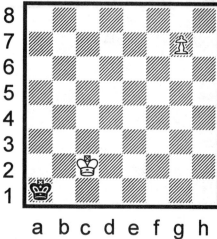

Diagram 2

Diagram 3

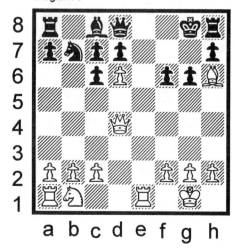

Diagram 4

Diagram 5

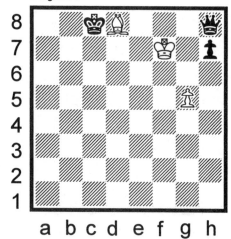

Diagram 6

Combination Quiz--Level II
(WHITE TO MOVE)

Diagram 1

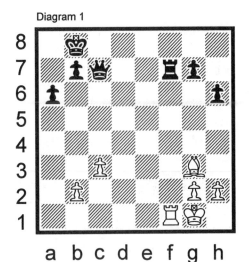

Diagram 2

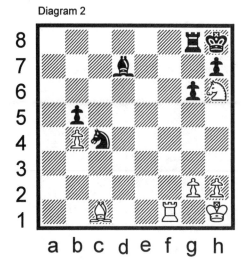

Diagram 3

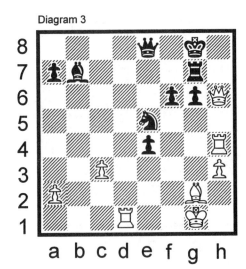

Diagram 4

Diagram 5

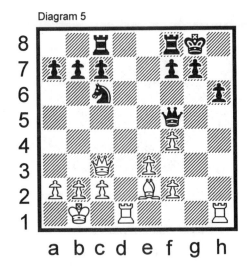

Diagram 6

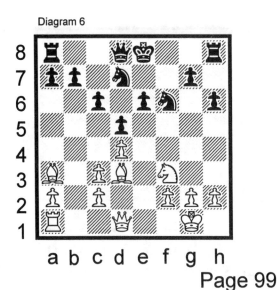

Combination Quiz--Level II
(WHITE TO MOVE)

Diagram 1

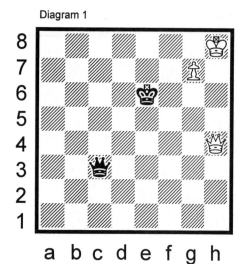

Diagram 2

Diagram 3

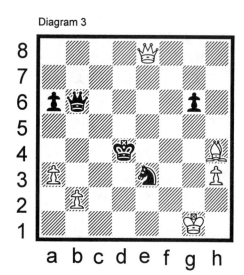

Diagram 4

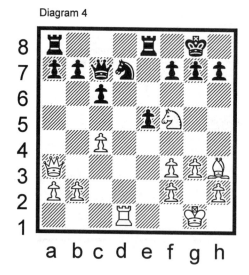

Diagram 5

Diagram 6

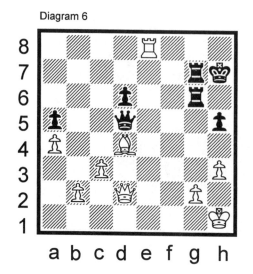

Forced Mate In Three
(WHITE TO MOVE)

Diagram 1

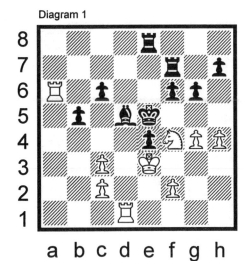

Diagram 2

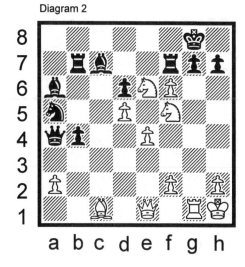

Diagram 3

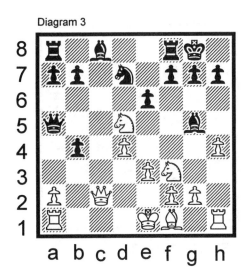

Diagram 4

Diagram 5

Diagram 6

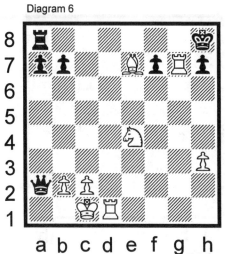

Forced Mate In Three
(WHITE TO MOVE)

Diagram 1

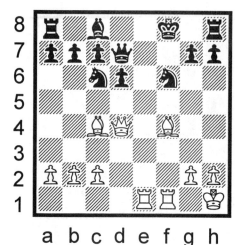

Diagram 2

Diagram 3

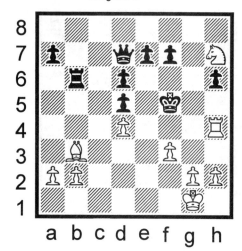

Diagram 4

Diagram 5

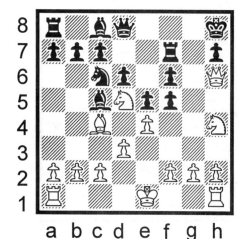

Diagram 6

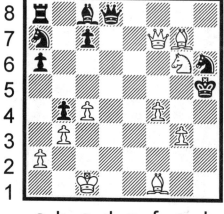

Forced Mate In Three
(WHITE TO MOVE)

Diagram 1

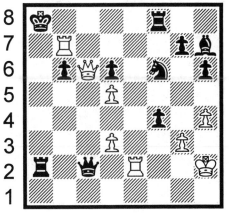

Diagram 2

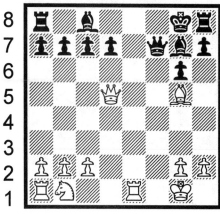

Diagram 3

Diagram 4

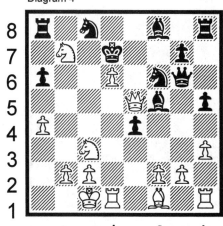

Diagram 5

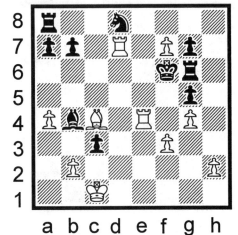

Diagram 6

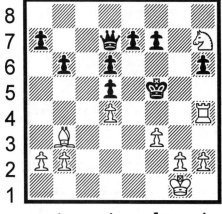

Forced Mate In Three
(WHITE TO MOVE)

Diagram 1

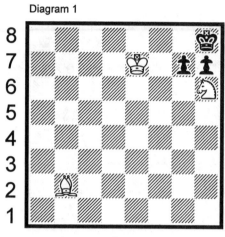

Diagram 2

Diagram 3

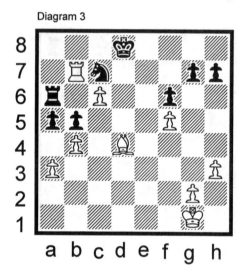

Diagram 4

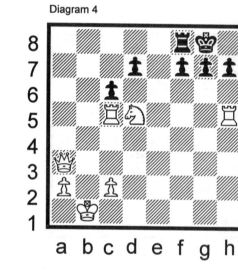

Diagram 5

Diagram 6

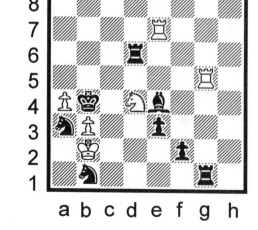

Forced Mate In Three
(WHITE TO MOVE)

Diagram 1

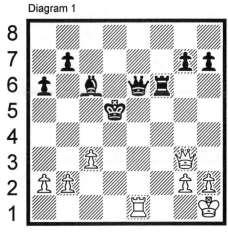

Diagram 2

Diagram 3

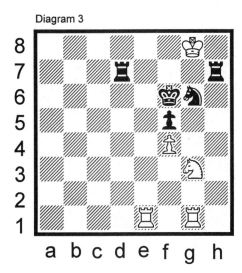

Diagram 4

Diagram 5

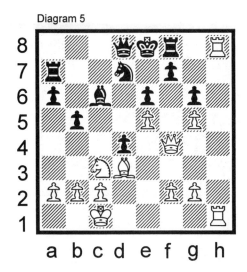

Diagram 6

Forced Mate In Three
(WHITE TO MOVE)

Diagram 1

Diagram 2

Diagram 3

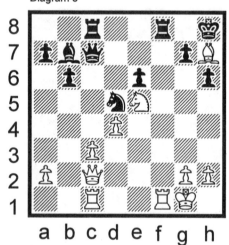

Diagram 4

Diagram 5

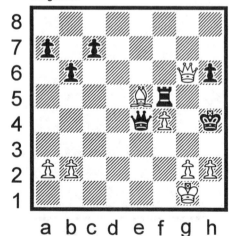

Diagram 6

Forced Mate In Three
(WHITE TO MOVE)

Diagram 1

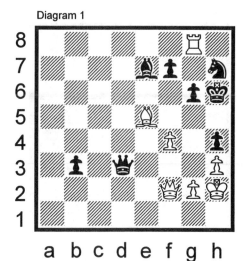

Diagram 2

Diagram 3

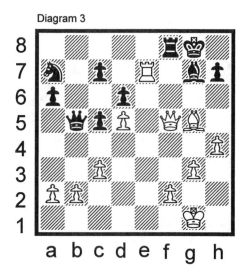

Diagram 4

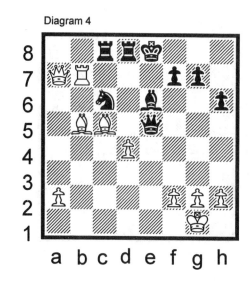

Diagram 5

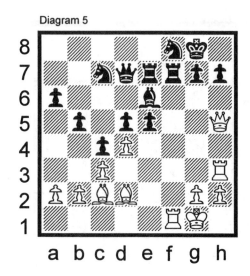

Diagram 6

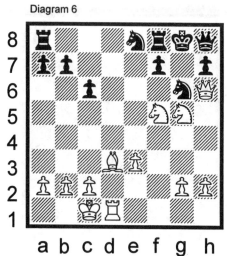

Multi-Option Forced Mate In Three
(WHITE TO MOVE)

Diagram 1

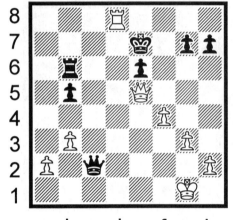

Diagram 2

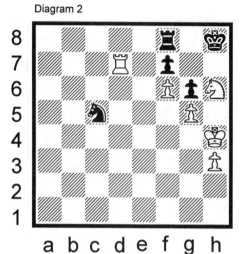

Diagram 3

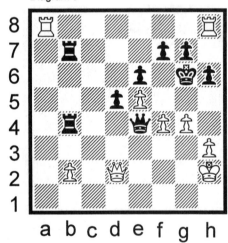

Diagram 4

Diagram 5

Diagram 6

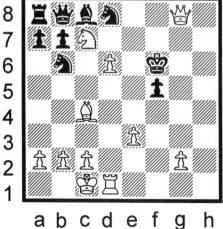

Multi-Option Forced Mate In Three
(WHITE TO MOVE)

Diagram 1

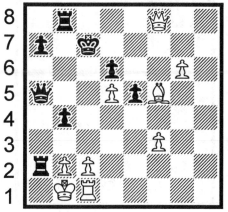

a b c d e f g h

Diagram 2

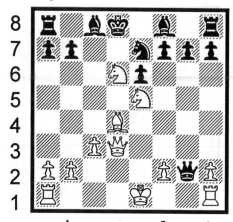

a b c d e f g h

Diagram 3

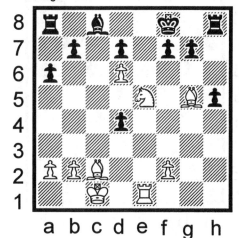

a b c d e f g h

Diagram 4

a b c d e f g h

Diagram 5

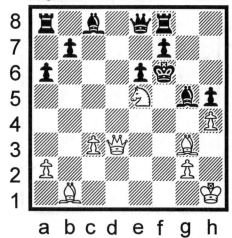

a b c d e f g h

Diagram 6

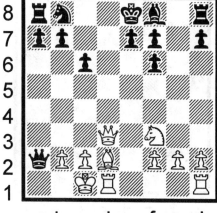

a b c d e f g h

Multi-Option Forced Mate In Three
(WHITE TO MOVE)

Diagram 1

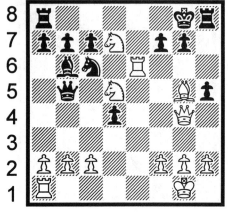

Diagram 2

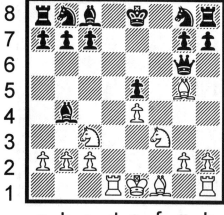

Diagram 3

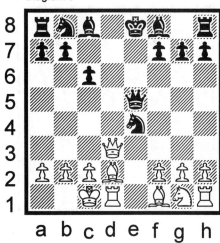

Diagram 4

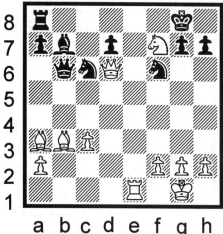

Diagram 5

Diagram 6

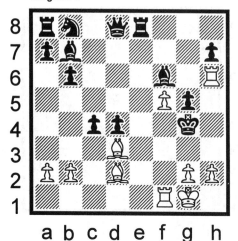

Ruy Lopez Quickies
(WHITE TO MOVE)

Diagram 1

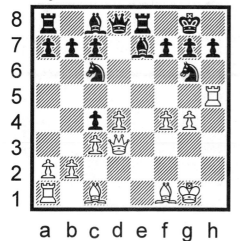

Diagram 2

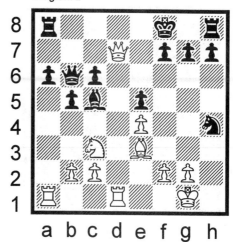

Diagram 3

Diagram 4

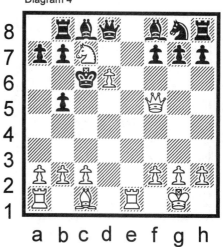

Diagram 5

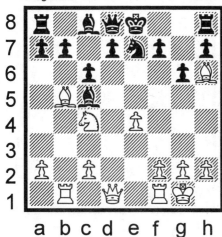

Diagram 6

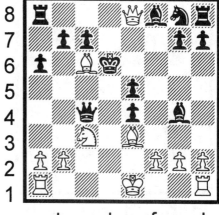

Combination Quiz--Level III
(WHITE TO MOVE)

Diagram 1

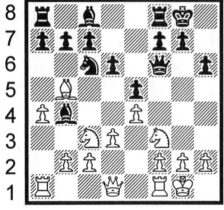

Diagram 2

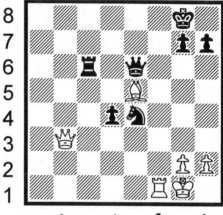

Diagram 3

Diagram 4

Diagram 5

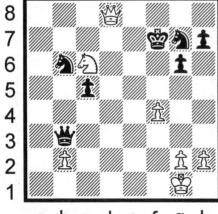

Diagram 6

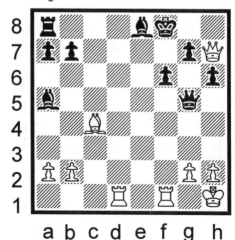

Combination Quiz--Level III
(WHITE TO MOVE)

Diagram 1

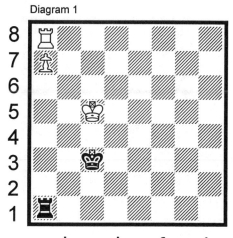

Diagram 2

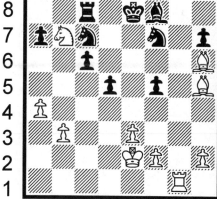

Diagram 3

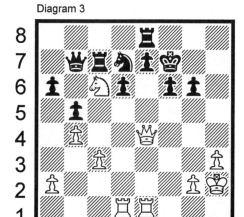

Diagram 4

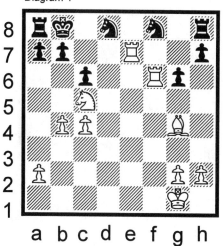

Diagram 5

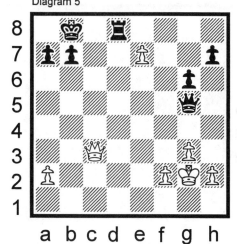

Diagram 6

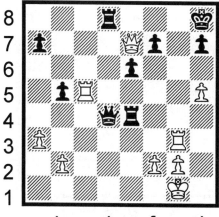

Combination Quiz--Level III
(WHITE TO MOVE)

Diagram 1

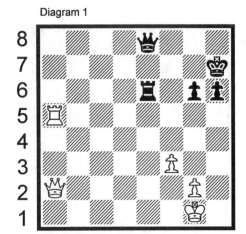

Diagram 2

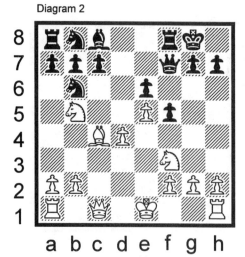

Diagram 3

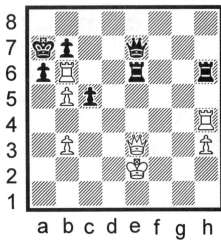

Diagram 4

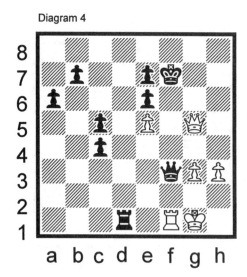

Diagram 5

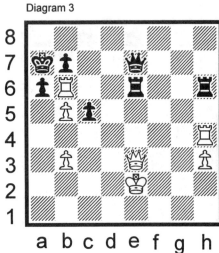

Diagram 6

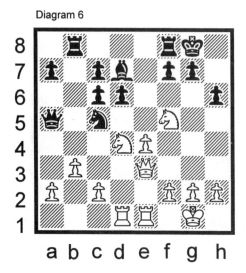

Combination Quiz--Level III
(WHITE TO MOVE AND MATE)

Diagram 1

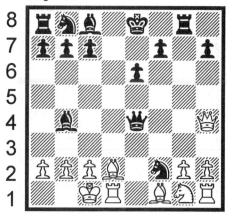

Diagram 2

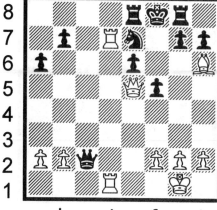

Diagram 3

Diagram 4

Diagram 5

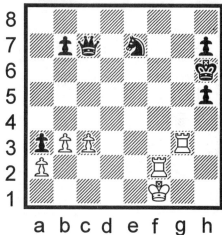

Diagram 6

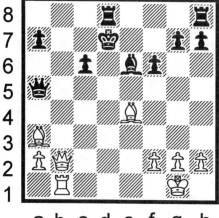

Combination Quiz--Level III
(WHITE TO MOVE)

Diagram 1

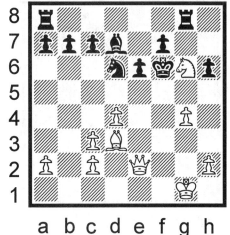

Diagram 2

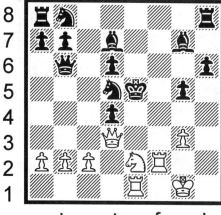

Diagram 3

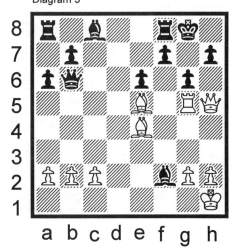

Diagram 4

Diagram 5

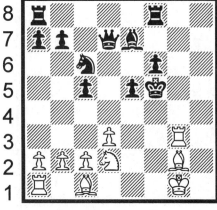

Diagram 6

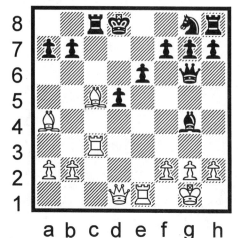

Page 116

Combination Quiz--Level III
(WHITE TO MOVE AND MATE)

Diagram 1

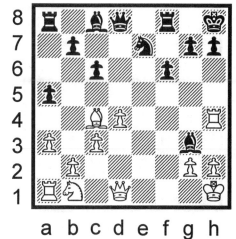

Diagram 2

Diagram 3

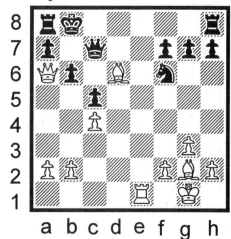

Diagram 4

Diagram 5

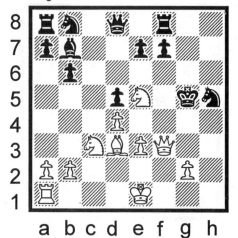

Diagram 6

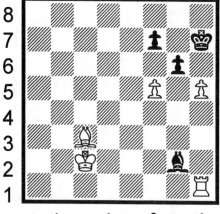

Combination Quiz--Level III
(WHITE TO MOVE)

Diagram 1

Diagram 2

Diagram 3

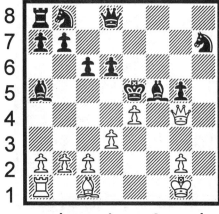

Diagram 4

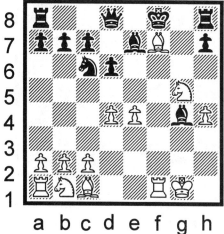

Diagram 5

Diagram 6

Combination Quiz--Level III
(WHITE TO MOVE AND MATE)

Diagram 1

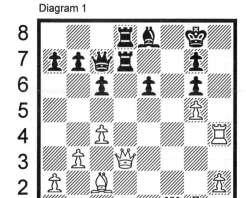

Diagram 2

Diagram 3

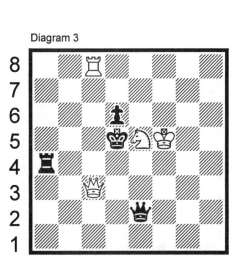

Diagram 4

Diagram 5

Diagram 6

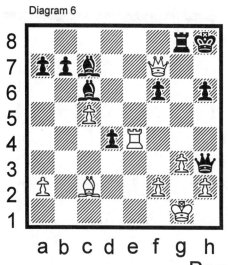

Combination Quiz--Level III
(WHITE TO MOVE)

Diagram 1

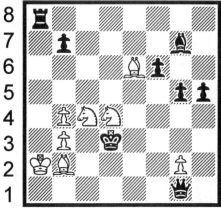

Diagram 2

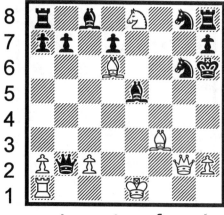

Diagram 3

Diagram 4

Diagram 5

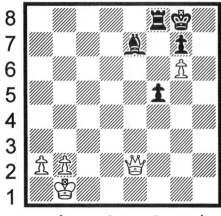

Diagram 6

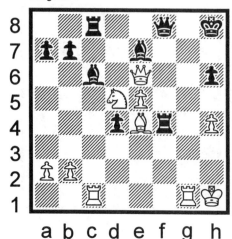

More Mate In One
(WHITE TO MOVE)

Diagram 1

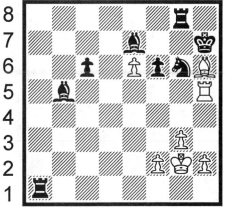

Diagram 2

Diagram 3

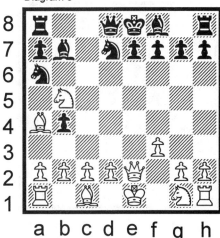

Diagram 4

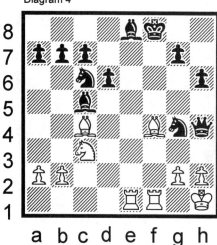

Diagram 5

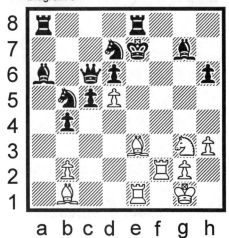

Diagram 6

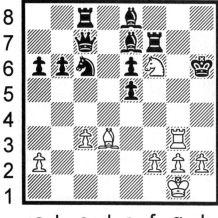

More Mate In One
(WHITE TO MOVE)

Diagram 1

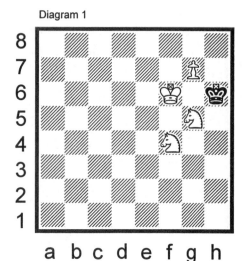

Diagram 2

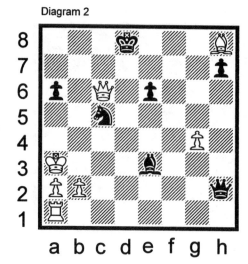

Diagram 3

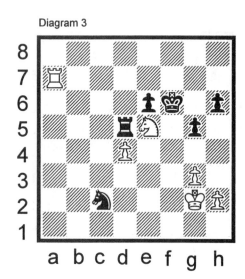

Diagram 4

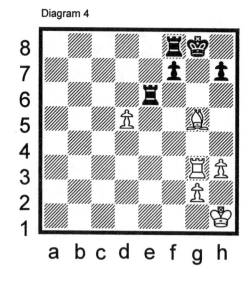

Diagram 5

Diagram 6

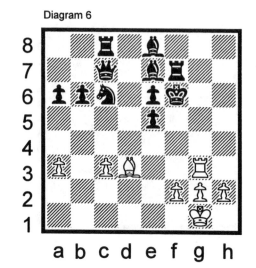

More Mate in One
(WHITE TO MOVE)

Diagram 1

Diagram 2

Diagram 3

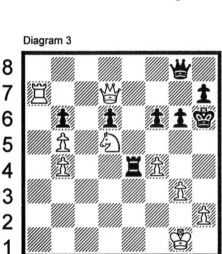

Diagram 4

Diagram 5

Diagram 6

More Mate In One
(WHITE TO MOVE)

Diagram 1

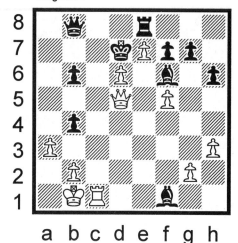

Diagram 2

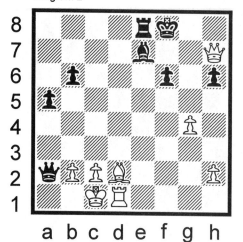

Diagram 3

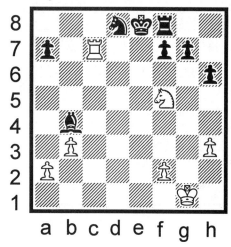

Diagram 4

Diagram 5

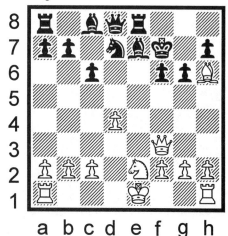

Diagram 6

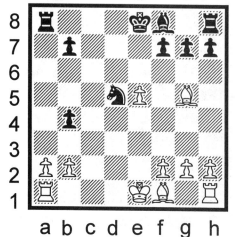

Page 124

More Mate In One
(WHITE TO MOVE)

Diagram 1

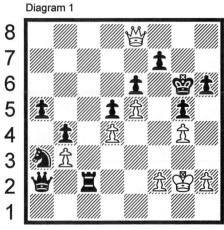

Diagram 2

Diagram 3

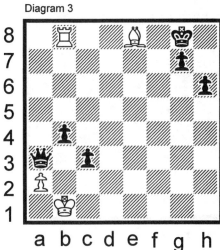

Diagram 4

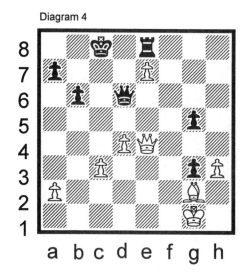

Diagram 5

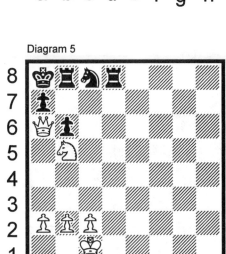

Diagram 6

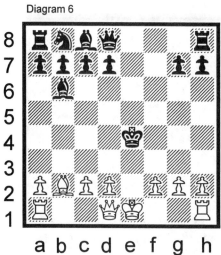

More Mate In One
(WHITE TO MOVE)

Diagram 1

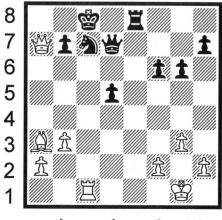

Diagram 2

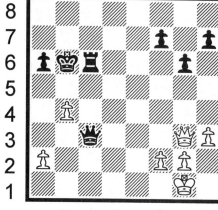

Diagram 3

Diagram 4

Diagram 5

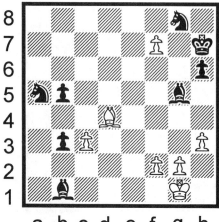

Diagram 6

Texas Tactics--Herding The King
(WHITE TO MOVE)

Diagram 1

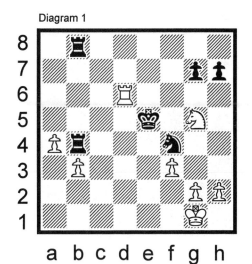

Diagram 2

Diagram 3

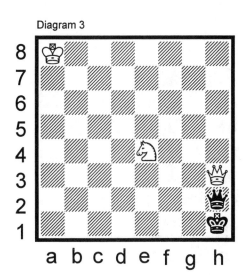

Diagram 4

Diagram 5

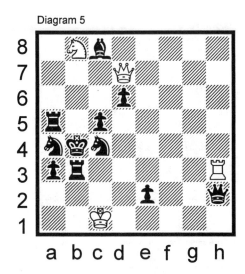

Diagram 6

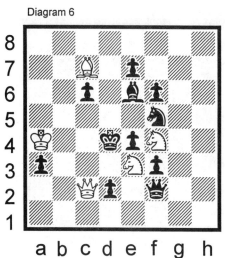

Unexpected Moves
(WHITE TO MOVE)

Diagram 1

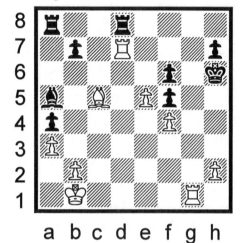

Diagram 2

Diagram 3

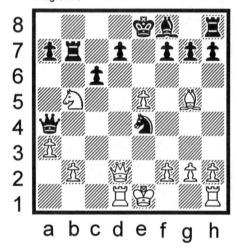

Diagram 4

Diagram 5

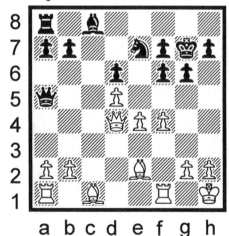

Diagram 6

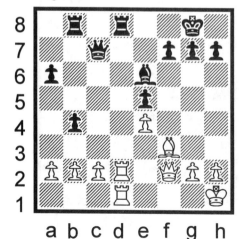

More Mate In Two
(WHITE TO MOVE)

Diagram 1

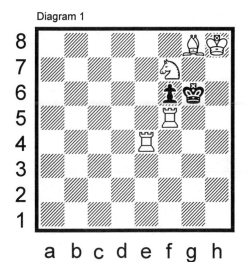

Diagram 2

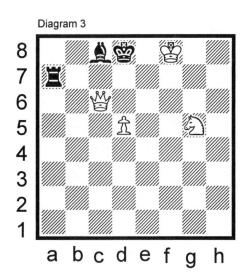

Diagram 3

Diagram 4

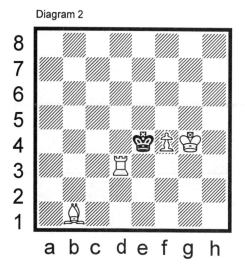

Diagram 5

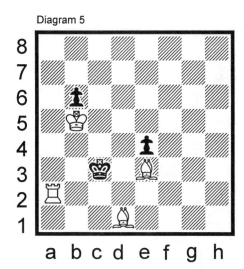

Diagram 6

More Mate In Two
(WHITE TO MOVE)

Diagram 1

Diagram 2

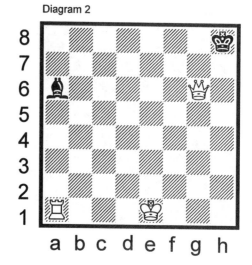

Diagram 3

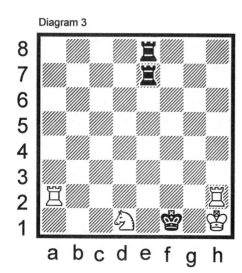

Diagram 4

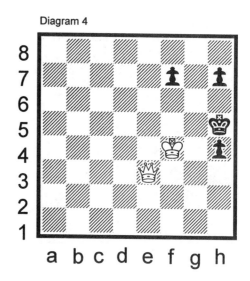

Diagram 5

Diagram 6

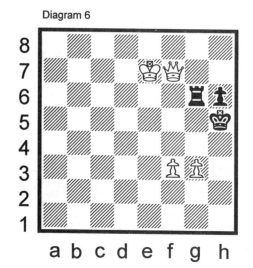

More Mate In Two
(WHITE TO MOVE)

Diagram 1

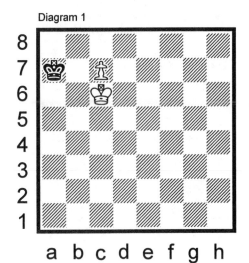

Diagram 2

Diagram 3

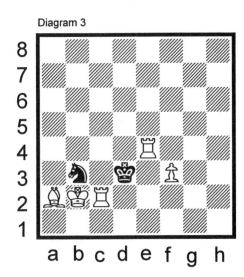

Diagram 4

Diagram 5

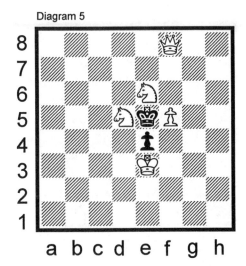

Diagram 6

Draw by Repetition

A player can earn a draw if a position is repeated three times. This can be very helpful when a player is facing a position they would otherwise lose. Find the draw in each position.

Diagram 1, Black to move

Diagram 2, White to move

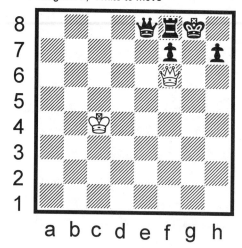

Diagram 3, White to move

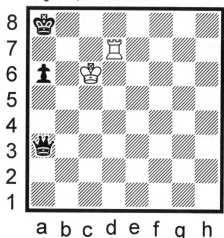

Diagram 4, Black to move

Diagram 5, White to move

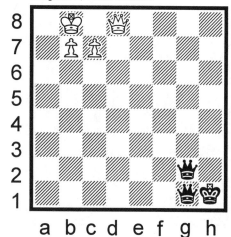

Diagram 6, Black to move

Paul Morphy vs. The Duke of Brunswick and Count Isourd
a consultation game played in Paris, 1858

The chess career of New Orlean's resident Pau Morphy was a short one. In a two-year period he rose to become the world's best before he retired. He displayed a knowledge of advanced principles that his peers never grasped. The following game is a legendary example of his aggressive style of play and knowledge of opening principles. It was played in a box at the Paris Opera during a performance of "The Barber of Seville".

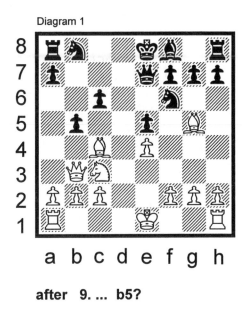

Diagram 1

after   9. ... b5?

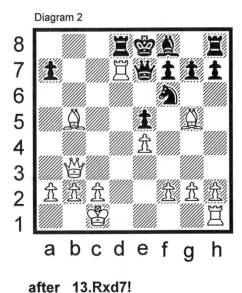

Diagram 2

after   13.Rxd7!

| 1.e4 | e5 |
| 2.Nf3 | d6 |

This opening is named after Andre Danican Philidor (1726-1795), a leading French chess player of the 18th century.

| 3.d4 | Bg4 |

A mistake already! Better is 3....Nd7 or 3....Nf6

| 4.dxe5 | Bxf3 |

Black would lose a pawn after 4....dxe5 5.Qxd8+ Kxd8 6.Nxe5

| 5.Qxf3 | dxe5 |
| 6.Bc4 | |

White is already making Black suffer for 3....Bg4?

| 6.... | Nf6? |

Black Has failed to see ahead to White's double attack.

| 7.Qb3! | Qe7 |
| 8.Nc3 | |

Of course White could win a pawn with Qxb7, but Morphy didn't want Black to exchange queens with 8.... Qb4+

| 8.... | c6 |
| 9.Bg5 | b5? (Diagram 1) |

The Duke and Count should be developing their pieces with 9....Qc7. Their aggression is misplaced.

10.Nxb5!	cxb5
11.Bxb5+	Nbd7
12.O-O-O	

White Castles with an attack!

| 12.... | Rd8 |

13Rxd7! (diagram 2)

White controls all the lines of attack to the Black King. Morphy follows with an elegant combination and a Rook and Bishop mate that bears his name.

13....	Rxd7
14.Rd1	Qe6
15.Bxd7+	Nxd7
16.Qb8+	Nxb8
17.Rxd8++	

ANSWERS

PAGE 1
1..Rc8++
2..Ra8++
3..Rh5++
4..Rd8++
5..Rd8++
6..Rd8++

PAGE 2
1..Rc8++
2..Rc8++
3..Rb8++
4..Rxg8++
5..Re5++
6..Ra1++

PAGE 3
1..Qxb7++
2..Qc7++
3..Qc8++
4..Qc6++(epaulette mate)
5..Qf7++
6..Qe7++

PAGE 4
1..Qe8++
2..Qh7++
3..Qa7++
4..Qh8++
5..Qh8++
6..Qxh7++

PAGE 5
1..Nf7++(smothered mate)
2..Bg7++
3..Bxf7++
4..Ba6++
(if 1.Bf5+ Re6 2.Bxe6++)
5..Bd3++
6..Nh6++

PAGE 6
1..1.Nb3++
2..1.Be5++
3..1.Bf6++
4..1.Bd5++
5..1.Nb6++
6..1.Nc2++

PAGE 7
1..1.Nc2++
2..1.Ne6++
3..1.Nc6++
4..1.Nc2++

5..1.Nxf7++
6..1.Bh7++

PAGE 8
1..1.b7++
2..1.h7++
3..1.g4++
4..1.d6++
5..1.g3++
6..1.g4++

PAGE 9
1..1.f8=Q or R++
2..1.Nb6++
3..1.c8=N++
4..1.c8=Q or R++
5..1.d8=Q or B++
6..1.dxe8=Q++

PAGE 10
1..1.Ng6++
2..1.Qf5++ or Rxd6++
3..1.Nb6++
4..1.Rd8++
5..1.Rf8++
6..1.Rd4++

PAGE 11
1..1.Qe5++
2..1.Rxh7++
3..1.Bf7++
4..1.Rh6++
5..1.Rh8++
6..1.Rxh7++

PAGE 12
1..Qf8++
2..Qf7++
3..Bc8++
4..Nf7++
5..Rh3++
6..Ne7++

PAGE 13
1..b4++
2..cxb6(e.p.)++
(Black's last move was b7 to b5)
3..O-O++
4..Qa6++
5..b8=N++
6..exd6(e.p.)++
(Black's last move was d7 to d5)

PAGE 14
1..Rxf5

2..Qxb7
3..Rxe7
4..Bxa8
5..Rxe6 or Bxe6
6..Rxd7

PAGE 15
1..Bh6
2..Re1
3..Qxb5
4..Bxc6+
5..Rxe4
6..Nxe5 if 6... dxe5 7.Qd8++

PAGE 16
1..Bd4
2..Rh4
3..Kg4! (attack pinned pieces!)
4..1.Nh5 then 2.Nxg7 draws
5..Nxg6+
6..1.Rxc3 (if 1.....Bxc3 then 2.Qf8++)

PAGE 17
1..Bf8 wins material
2..Bc4
3..f5
4..Bf4
5..c6
6..c4

PAGE 18
1..Rc5! (a crosspin)
2..Re1
3..Qe4!
4..Rf7
5..Rd1
6..Nxf4 with a drawn ending.

PAGE 19
1..Bc7
2..Qa7
3..Kb2
4..Ke3
5..Ng5
6..Bg5

1..1.Re1! (1....Rxe1 2.Qxc6 wins a piece or 1....Kd7 2.Rxe6 Kxe6 3.Qxc6+ also works)
2..1.Rd8+ Kh7 2.Rh8++
3..1.Nb6+ cxb6 2.Be6 wins the Queen (line clearance)
4..Bg8! double attack!
5..Nxh4! wins a pawn
6..Re8! removes the guard. (if 1....Qxe8 2.Bxf6+ Kg8 3.Qh8++)

1..1.Rc8+ Rd8 2.Qb5! (2...Qxb5 3.Rd8++ or 2...Qd4 3.Qe8+ leads to mate)
2..White wins by cutting off the escape square. 1.Nd5! (1...exd5 2.Qh7+ Kf8 3.Qh8++) or 1.Qh7+ Kf8 2.Nd5! works.
3..1.Rxc6+ Qxc6 2.Ne7+ wins
4..1.Qc4+ Kb8 2.Rxd7 and White wins the exchange after 2...Qxd7 3.Qxg8+ If 2...Qe8 3.Qc7+ and mate next move.
5..White takes advantage of her active pieces and the pin on f7. 1.Nf6+ Bxf6 2.Qxg6 Bg7 3.Qh7++.
6. 1.Qh5+ Rxh5 2.Bg6++

1..(Attraction) 1.Rf8+! Kxf8 2.Bxg7+ Kxg7 3.Qxd5 wins
2..(Attraction) 1.Rh8! Kxh8 2.Bf7++ with a discovery.
3..(Bishop Power!) 1.Rxh6+ gxh6 2.Bf7++
4..1.Nf6+(Dbl. Check) Kh8 2.Ng6++
5..(Attraction & Pawn Promotion) 1.Bh7+ Kf7 or Kh7 2.g8=Q++
6..(Attraction) 1.Qe7+! Kxe7 2.Ng6+

(Dbl. Check) Kd8 3.Nf7++

1..1.Qxg7+ Kxg7 2.h8=Q+ Rxh8 3.Rg4+ King Moves 4.Rh1++
2..(Overloaded Defender) 1.Bh6! Re8 2.Bg7 wins the exchange. Bad for Black is 1....Nxh6 2.Ne7+ losing the Queen.
3..(Overload) 1.Rxc7! the Queen can't defend h8 and the rook at c1 at the same time.
4..(Overload) 1.Rf2! with the two threats of Qg6++ and Qxc6. 1....Re6 expecting 2.Rxc2 fails because of an in-between move 2.Qf8+
5..1.Qxd4+ Qxd4 2.Ne6+ wins a piece.
6..(Attraction into a Fork!) 1.Qxe7+! Kxe7 2.Nxd5+ wins.

1..1.Bxg6 wins. (1...hxg 2.h7)
2..1.b6 axb 2.c6! or 1...cxb 2.a6 and one of the pawns will promote.

3..1.Nb4 Kf7 2.Nxc6! if 2...bxc 3.b7 and if 2...Ke8 3.Nb8 and White wins on the Queenside.
4..1.Bh5! gxh 2.g6 and the pawns can't be stopped. If 1...Bc4 2.Bxg6 and the pawns fall.
5..1.Nxg7 Nxg7 2.h6 and Black can't cover the queening square.
6..1.Qc8+ Kh7 2.Qxe6! wins. If 2...fxe 3.f7 and the pawn advances.

1..1.Qxc8+ Rxc8 2.Ne6 wins.
2..(Double Attack set up by a Skewer) 1.Bc7! Rxc7 2.Qe5! and White

threatens 3.Qxg7++ and 3.Qxc7 winning the exchange.
3..1.Nxe5 Bxe5 2.Rg8++ or 1....dxe5 2.Rxc6
4..(Double Attack) 1.Nxe7+ Qxe7 2.Qd5+ wins the Knight.
5..(Remove the Defense) 1.Qxc3 Nxc3 2.Ne7+ wins the exchange.
6..(A Trapped Piece) 1.Rd4! and the Bishop has no escape. 1....Bc5 2.b4 wins or 1....Be1 2.b4

1..1.Rxb6 axb6 2.Bd5+
2..1.Rf5 and Black loses either the Knight or Bishop
3..1.Rg6+ wins the Knight
4..1.Rxe4 Rxe4 2.Qc6 wins a rook
5..1.Qxf8 Rxf8 2.Ng7+ wins
6..1.Rg7!! the threat is 2.Nf5++ (1....Kxg7 2.Ne6+ wins)

1..1.Qxf6+ Nxf6 2.Bxf6++
2..1.Qxf8+ Kxf8 2.e7++
3..1.Qxg4+ Kxg4 2.Be2++
4..1.Qb8+ Nxb8 2.Rd8++
5..1.Qg6+ hxg 2.Ng7++ or 1.....Rf7 2.Qxf7++
6..1.Qg6 fxg 2.Nh7++ (1....Kg8 2.Qxf7+ Kh8 3.Qxh5+ Bh6 4.Qxh6++)

PAGE 44
1..1.Rd6+ Rxd6 (if
1...Qd7 2.Qxd7++)
2.Nxe6++
2..1.Qh7+ Kxh7
2.Bf7++
3..1.Qe7+ Rxe7
2.Nf6++
4..1.Bg5+ Kxf7
2.Nd6++
5..1.Nf5+ Ke8
2.Nxg7++
6..1.Qf7+ Nxf7
2.Ne6++

PAGE 45
1..1.Rg7+ Kh8 2.Rg8++
2..1.Re7+ Kh8 2.Rh7++
3..1.Bf6+ Kxf6 or Kh6
2.Qg5++
4..1.Rg4+ Kh6 or Kh8
2.Nxf7++
5..1.Nf8+ Kh8 2.Qh7++
6..1.Re5+ Kd6 2.c5++

PAGE 46
1..1.Nf6+ Kf8 2.Qe8++
2..1.Rb4+ Ka5 2.Bc7++
3..1.Qg7+ Bxg7
2.Nf6++
4..1.Nf7+ Kg8 2.Nh6++

PAGE 46...cont.
5..1.Rxe8+ Rxe8 or Kh7
2.Qxg7++
6..1.Qg8+ Nxg8
2.Nf7++

PAGE 47
1..1.Rxh5+ Kxh5
2.Rh7++
2..1.Bb5+ Ke7 2.Nd5++
3..1.Bg5+ Kg6
2.N2f4++
4..1.b8=Q+ Nxb8
2.Rd8++
5..1.Ng6+ Kf7
2.Nxh8++
6..1.Re7! Any Move
for Black 2.Re8++

PAGE 48
1..1.Rg8 b5
2.axb(e.p.)++
2..1.Qxc3+ Nxc3
2.b4++
3..1.Qg6+! Nxg6
2.fxg6++(1.f6 also wins)
4..1.Bf7+ Kg4 3.h3++

5..1.d5+ cxd 2.cxd++
(2.exd+ Kf5 and Black
escapes)
6..1.Rxh7+ Kg5 2.h4++

PAGE 49
1..1.Rh8+ Kxh8
2.Qh7++ (1....Qxh8
2.Qf7++)
2..1.Rxh6+ gxh6
2.Qf7+
3..1.Nxh7+ Nxh7
2.Ng6++
4..1.Qc7+ Nxc7
2.Nb6++
5..1.Qxh7+ Kf7
2.Qxg7++
6..1.Rg7+ Kxg7
2.Qh7++

PAGE 50
1..1.Bd3+ Kxa4
2.Qc2++
2..1.Rxd8+ Kxg7
2.Qg5++
3..1.Rxh6+ Kg8
2.Ne7++
4..1.Qa8+ Rxa8
2.Rxa8++
5..1.Qxh6 gxh6
2.Bh7++
6..1.Bh6+ Kxg6
2.Qg4++

PAGE 51
1..1.Qxc6+ bxc
2.Ba6++
2..1.Rxf7+ Kxf7 or Kg8
2.Qg7++
3..1.Qxh7+ Kxh7+
2.Rh5++
4..1.Nh6+ Kf8 2.Nh7++
5..1.Qxh7+ Kxh7
2.Rh4++
6..1.Qxh7+ Rxh7
2.Rg8++

PAGE 52
1..1.Qxg7+ Kxg7
2.Bc3++
2..1.Qe7+ Kg8 2.Nh6++
3..1.Qf5 h5 2.Qxh5++
4..1.Qf8+ Rxf8
2.Rxf8++
5..1.d7+ Bxd7 or Qxd7
2.Qf8++
6..1.Qh5+ Kxh5
2.Rh7++

PAGE 53

1..1.a3+ Ka4 2.b3++
2..1.Bf4+ Ke4 2.Bf3++
or Bg6++
3..1.Qxf6! gxf
2.Bxf6++ (1....any other
move 2.Qxg7++)
4..1.Qxh6+ Kxh6
2.Rh4++ (if 1....Kg8
2.Qh8++)
5..1.Ng5+ Kg8 or Kh8
2.Rd8++
6..1.Qxh7+ Qxh7
2.Nf7++

PAGE 54
1..1.Bf6+ any move
2.Qxg8++
2..1.Bd5+ Nxd5
2.exd5++
3..1.Rh8+ Kxh8
2.Qxf8++
4..1.Rxf7+ Nxf7
2.Ng6++
5..1.Qd2+ Qe3
2.Qxe3++
6..1.Bf5+ Kd6 2.Be7++

PAGE 55
1..1.Qf7+ Rxf7
2.exf7++
2..1.Qe8! a1=Q
2.Qh5++
3..1.Nc6 a5 or Kb7
2.Rxb8++
4..1.Qf3 any black
move 2.Qg3++
5..1.Rd8+ Kc5 2.Qd4++
6..1.Bg2! Bxg2
2.Qxg2++ or 1.... a5
2.Bxf3++

PAGE 56
1..1.Rxg7+ Kxg7
2.Qxh6++
2..1.Rh5+ Kg7
2.Rxg6++
3..1.Qf7+ Nxf7
2.exf7++
4..1.Ng6+ hxg6
2.Rh1++
5..1.Rh6! c4 2.Rf5++
6..1.Nc7+ Kd8 2.Nf7++

PAGE 57
1..1.Rxe6+ Kxe6
2.Qf7++
2.. (Decoy the Knight)
1.Qf5+ Nxf5 2.e6++
3..1.Nb5 Ke8 2.Nd6++
4..1.Qh5+ Kf6 2.Qg5++
5..1.Qg7+ Qxg7
2.fxg7++
6..1.Ng6+ Kg7
2.Rxf8++

PAGE 58
1..1.Qc8+ Rxc8
2.Nd7++
2..1.Qe8+ Bxe8
2.Rxe8++
3..1.Rxd8+ Kxd8
2.Re8++
4..1.Bxd4+ Rxd4
2.Rf8++
5..1.h7+ Kf8 2.h8=Q++
6..1.Rd8+ Bf8
2.Rxf8++

PAGE 59
1..1.Rh5+ gxh5
2.Nf5++
2..1.h7+ Kh8 2.Nxg6++
3..1.Rh5+ Nxh5 2.g5++
4..1.Ng6+ hxg 2.Rh1++
5..1.bxc6+ any move
2.Qb7++
6..1.f6+ Kg8 2.Rd8++

PAGE 60
1..1.Qg4+ Qxg4
2.Nf6++
2..1.Qa4+ Rxa4 (if
1...b5 or Kg8 2.Qxa8+
leads to mate) 2.c8=Q++
3..1.Rxa7+ Bxa7
2.Nc7++
4..1.Qxg7+ Nxg7
2.Nh6++
5..1.Qf8+ Rxf8
(1...Rg7 2.Bxg7++ or
Qxg7++) 2.Bg7++
6..1.Rc8+ Nxc8 2.Qd8++

PAGE 61
1..1.Rc8+ Rxc8
2.Qxc8++
2..1.Bb5+ c6 2.Re7++
3..1.Qc4+ Kh8 2.Qc8++
4..1.Rg8+ Kxg8
2.Rg1++
5..1.f7+ Rxf7 2.Rh8++
6..1.Nb7+ Ke8 2.Rc8++

PAGE 62
1..1.Rh7+ Kxg8 2.Rh8++
2..1.Qxa5+ Kb8
2.Rd8++
3..1.f7+ Ke7 2.Bg5++
4..1.Qxh7+ Kxh7
2.Rh3++
5..1.Qe6+ Kc7 2.Bd6++
6..1.Rb7+ Kc8 2.Ra8++

PAGE 63
1..1.Na6+ bxa6
2.Qb4++
2..1.Qc8+ Ke7 2.Re6++
3..1.Qxh7+ Kxh7
2.Rh3++
4..1.Qxf7+ Kd8
2.Qxe7++
5..1.Re7+ Kc8 2.Be6++
6..1.Rd8+ Rg8 2.c4++

PAGE 64
1..1.Qxh6+ Qxh6
2.Rxg8++
2..1.Ng7+ Kf4 2.Ne2++
3..1.Qg6+ Nxg6
2.fxg6++
4..1.Bh6+ Kg8
2.Rxe8++
5..1.Rxc6+ Qxc6
2.Qb4++
6..1.Nh4+ Ke6 2.d5++

PAGE 65
1..1.Bf6+ Nxf6
2.exf6++
2..1.Rg8+ Kxg8
2.Re8++
3..1.Rf5+ Rg5 or Bxf5
2.Rfxg5++
4..1.Rh5! gxh5
2.Qf6++ (otherwise
2.Qxh7++)
5..1.Nf5+ Kh5 2.Qh4++
6..1.Re8+ Nxe8
2.Qf8++

PAGE 66
1..1.Qg6+ hxg6
2.Bxg6++
2..1.Nh6+ Kf8
2.Nxe6++
3..Qxe8+ Rxe8
2.Rxe8++
4..1.Ne7+ Kh8
2.Qxf8++
5..1.Rexf8+ Nxf8
2.Bf7++
6..1.Bg7+ Kg8 2.Nf6++

PAGE 67
1..1.Rg7+ Kxg7
2.Qh7++
2..1.Rf7+ Kg8 2.Qe8++
3..1.Bd5+ Kh8 2.Rf8++
4..1.Qf7+ ! Kxf7
2.Rd8++
5..1.Bc6+ Kd8 2.Qd7++
6..Ne7+ Kh8 2.Nxg6++

PAGE 68
1..1.Ra8+ Bxa8
2.Qc8++
2..1.Ne6+ Ke8 2.Qd8++
3..1.Bxb6+ Ke7
2.Nd5++
4..1.Bxf7+ Qxf7
2.Qd8++
5..1.Rad1 Bxg4
2.Rd3++
6..1.Rf5+ gxf5
2.Rg5++

PAGE 69
1..1.Nxa7+ Kd7
2.Bb5++
2..1.Qxc7+ Kxc7
2.Rc5++
3..1.Nxe6+ fxe6 (the
Queen can't be saved!)
2.Qxe6++
4..1.Re8+ Rxe8
2.Rxe8++
5..1.Rxg7+ Kxg7
2.Qxh7++
6..1.Rxb8+ Rxb8
2.Rxb8++

PAGE 70
1..1.Ng5+ Kg8
2.Qxh7++
2..1.Bf5+ Kd6 2.Be7++
3..1.Qe8+ Nxe8
2.Rf8++
4..1.Rg6+ fxg6
2.Qxg6++ or 1.f5! Rxd3
2.Qg5++
5..1.Rxb7+ Kxb7
2.Qb6++
6..1.Qxd7+ Nxd7
2.Ne6++

PAGE 71

1..1.Qxh7+ Kxh7
2.Rh5++
2..1.Ng5+ hxg5
2.hxg6++
3..1.Nd7+ Ke8 2.Rg8++
4..1.Qxf6+ Rdxf6
2.Qg7++
5..1.Rg8+ Rxg8
2.Nf7++
6..1.Rh8+ Kxh8
2.Qh7++

PAGE 72

1..1.Ba6+ Kc7 2.Bf4++
2..1.Rh8+ Kxh8 2.f7++
3..1.Qg6+ Kh8
2.Qxh6++
4..1.Ra1+ Kb8 2.Ra8++
5..1.Rh5+ Kg2 2.Rh2++
6..1.Rg7+ Bxg7
2.Ne7++

PAGE 73

1..1.Ne7+ Kh8
2.Nxf7++
2..1.Nf6+ Kf8 2.Bc5++
3..1.Nc6+ Ke8 2.Re7++
4..1.Rg3+ Kh8 2.Nf7++
5..1.Nh6+ Kh8 2.Bc3++
6..1.Ne6+ Kmoves
2.Rh1++

PAGE 74

1..1.Qe6+ Bf2 (White
also threatens Qxf7++)
2.Rh8++
2..1.Re7+ Kf8
2.Rxd8++
3..1.Ne2+
4..1.Ne2+ Kf3 2.Qf5++
(if 1.... Kh3 2.Qh5++
5..1.Rh8+ Kf7 2.Rf8++

PAGE 74...cont.

6..1.Qh1+ Kxg4
2.Qf3++

PAGE 75

1..1.Ra7+ Kc8 2.Rc7++
2..1.Bxf7+ Ke7
2.Nd5++
3..1.Nhg6+ Kg8
2.Rh8++
4..1.Qh8+ Bxh8
2.Rxh8++
5..1.Qd8+ Kf7 2.Ne5++
6..1.Rxf8+ Kxf8
2.Re8++

PAGE 76

1..1.Bf5+ Kc7 2.Bd8++
2..1.Ba3+ Re7 2.g7++
3..1.Rxg6+ Rxg6
2.Qh8++
4..1.Qf6+ Nxf6
2.Be7++
5..1.Bf8 pawn moves
2.Ba3++
6..1.Rxf8+ Qxf8
2.Qxf8++

PAGE 77

1..1.Rg7+ Kf8 2.Rh8++
2..1.Nf6+ Kh8
2.Nxf7++
3..1.Nf6+ Kd8 2.Qe8++
4..1.Rf8+ Rxf8
2.Ng7++
5..1.Nf6+ gxf6
2.Bxf7++
6..1.c5+ Ke6 2.Qb3++

PAGE 78

1..1.Rxh7+ Kxh7
2.Qh5++
2..1.Bg5+ Kxf7
2.Nd6++
3..1.Rf8+ Ka7 2.Ra1++
4..1.Qxh7+ Kxh7
2.Rh3++
5..1.Rf8+ Kxf8
2.Qf7++
6..1.Qg8+ Rxg8
2.Nf7++

PAGE 79

1..1.Rxg5+ hxg5
2.Rxg5++
2..1.Bg2+ Rc6
2.Bxc6++
3..1.Rdxd8+ Qxd8
2.Ne7++
4..1.Nb6+ axb 2.Ra1++
5..1.Ng6+ hxg6
2.Qh3++
6..1.Nd6+ Kd8 2.Qe8++

PAGE 80

1..1.Qxh5 gxh5
2.Bh7++ or 1.Qxh5 Bxg5
2.Qh8++
2..1.Rxh6+ Kxh6
2.Qg6++ or 1.Rg8+ Rf5
2.Bxf5 or Qg6++
3..1.Qf8+ Kxf8
2.Rd8++ or 1.Qf8+ Kh7
2.Qg7++
4..1.Qf8+ Kh7 2.Qg7++
or 1.Qf8+ Bxf8 2.Rh8++

5..1.Rb8+ Nxb8
2.Qb7++ or 1.Rxc7+ Kxc7
or Nxc7 2.Qb7++
6..1.Re8+ Kxe8
2.Qe7++

PAGE 81

1..1.Rxg5+ hxg5
2.Qh8++ or 1.Rxg5+ fxg5
2.Ne7++
2..1.Ba4 bxa4(1.... b4
2.Bb5++) Rb6++
3..1.Qe4! g6 2.Qe8++
or 1.Qe4 Qd8 2.Qxh7++
4..1.Nc4+ Kc6 2.Be4++
or 1.Nc4+ Ka6 2.b5++
5..1.Bxe6+ dxe6
2.Qxh7++ or 1.Bxh7+ Kh8
2.Nf7++
6..1.Qh2 and White
wins with 2.Qh8++

PAGE 82

1..1.Qf7+ Nxf7
2.Ne6++
2..1.Nf6! Nxd3 or any
move 2.Rxh7 or Qxh7++
3..1.Nd6+ Nxd6
2.Qxb8++ or 1.....Qxd6
2.Qb7++
4..1.exf6+ Kxd6
2.Bf4++ or 1.....Kf8
2.Bh6++ or 1.....Kd8
2.f7++
5..1.Nf6+ K moves
2.Rg8++ or 1.Nh6+ K
moves 2.Rg8++
6..1.Nfe7+ Rxe7
2.Qf8++ or 1.Qg7+ Rxg7
2.Nh6++

PAGE 83

1..1.Rb6+ K moves
2.Rb8++
2..1.Nf6+ K moves
2.Re8++
3..1.Qxh7+ Kxh7
2.Rh3++ or Rh4++
4..1.Bxe7+ Rxe7
2.Rg6++ or 1.Rg6+ Nxg6
2.Rf7++ or 1.Rxe7 Rxe7
2.Rg6++ or mate with Rf7
or Rg6 or Nd7 depending
on Black's move.

5..1.Qxe5+ dxe5
2.Bc5++ or 1.....fxe5
2.Bg5++ or 1.....Be6
2.Qxe6++
6..1.R7f6+ Bxf6
2.Rxf6++ or 1.R1f6+
Bxf6 2.Rxf6++

PAGE 84
1..1.Re8+ Nxe8
2.Bh7++ or 1.Re8+ Rf8
2.gxf8=Q++
# 2..1.Qh6 any move
2.Qg7++
3..1.Rg8+ Kxg8
2.Qg7++ or Qh8++
4..1.Qc8+ Rxc8
2.Nd7++ or 1.Qe8+ Qd8
or Rxe8 2.Nd7++
5..1.a7+ Kc8 2.a8=Q++
or 2.a8=R++
6..1.h4+ Kxh4 2.Qg3++
or 1.....Kh6 2.Qxh5++

PAGE 85
1..1.Bb5+ Kf7 2.Be8++
or 1.....Kd8 2.Re8++
2..1.b8=Q Ka1 2.Qb2++
or 1.....Ka3 2.Qb3++
3..1.Rh2+ Kg1 2.Kd2++
or 2.O-O-O++
4..1.Kh2 e1=Q 2.Rh8++
or 1.....g6 or g5
2.Rd7++ 1......Rg2+ just
stalls.
5..1.Qxf7+ Rxf7
2.Bxf7++ or 1.Bxf7+
Rxf7 2.Qxf7++
6..1.Ra6+ bxa6
2.Qb4++ or 1.Qc5+ Ka4
2.b3++ or 1.Qc5+ b5
2.Qa3++

PAGE 86
1..1.Bb8! any move
2.Nc7++
2..1.Rxf8+ Kxf8
2.Qf7++ or 1.Rxg7+ Kh8
2.Rg8++ or Rxh7++
PAGE 86...cont.
3..1.Ne6 g6 2.hxg6++
or 1.....g5
2.hxg6(e.p.)++
4..1.Nxd7+ Qe7
2.Qxe7++ or 1.....any
other move for Black
2.Nf6++
5..1.Ke7 dxc 2.Nf6++
6..1.Rxf6 any move
2.Qxh7++

PAGE 87
1..1.Bf6+ Kxf6
2.Qh8++ or 1.Bf6+ Kh7
2.Qh8++
2..1.Nxe6+ Kh7
2.Qxg7++ or 1......f4
2.Qxg7++ or 1.....g5
2.hxg6(e.p.)++
3..1.Nc6+ Ke8 2.Nc7++
4..1.Rg5+ Rf7
2.Qxf7++ or 1.....Rxb3
2.Bxh7++ or 1.....Bd5
2.Bxh7++ or 1.Bxh7+
Qxh7 2.Rg5++
5..1.Rb Kd4 2.Rb4++
6..1.Rxc6+ Bxc6
2.Qe7++ or 1.....Qxc6
2.Qb4++

PAGE 88
1..1.exf7+ any move
2.Rxe8++
2..1.Nf3+ dxc3 2.Qa8++
3..1.Qh7+ Kg4 2.Qh3++
or 1.g4+ Kxg4 or Kh4
2.Qh3++ or 1.g4+ Kh5
2.Qh7++
4..1.Rhf1+ Kg8 2.Ne7
or Nf6++
5..1.Rxg8+ Rxg8
2.Nh7++ or 1.Nh7+ Rxh7
2.Rxg8++
6..1.d8=Q+ Kb7
2.Qc7++ or Qd7++ or
1.Qc6+ Kb8 2.d8=Q or
R++ or 2.Qc8++

PAGE 89
1..1.Rxh5+ gxh5
2.Qf6++ or 1.Qf4+ g5
2.Qf6++
2..1.Ne4+ Ke7 2.Qf7++
or 1.Nb5+ Ke7 2.Qf7++
3..1.Qb5+ Nxb5
2.Bxb5++
4..1.Bd5+ Ne6
2.Bxe6++ or 1.....Bxd5
2.Rf8++
5..1.Rxb6+ Ka7
2.Qb7++ or 1.Rxc7+ Kb8
2.Qb7++
6..1.Qxf7+ Kh8
2.Qxf8++ or 1.....Rxf7
2.Rd8++

PAGES 90-94, ITALIAN TACTICS
DIAGRAM 1.
1.e4 e5 2.Nf3 Nc6
3.Bc4 h6 4.c3 Nf6 5.d4
exd4 6.e5 Nh7 7.0-0
dxc3 8.Nxc3 Be7 9.Qd3
0-0 10.Qg6 d5 11.Nxd5
fxg6 and White mates
with 12.Nxe7+ Kh8
13.Nxg6 mate.

DIAGRAM 2.
1.e4 e5 2.Nf3 Nc6 3.
Bc4 Bc5 4.c3 Nf6 5.d4
exd4 6.e5 Ng4? 7.Bd5
Nxf2 8.Bxf7+ Kxf7
9.Ng5+ Kg8 and White
mates in 4 moves with
10.Qb3+ d5
11.exd6(e.p.)+ Be6
12.Qxe6+ Kf8 13.Qf7
mate.

DIAGRAM 3.
1.e4 e5 2.Nf3 Nc6
3.Bc4 Bc5 4.c3 Nf6
5.d4 exd4 6.cxd4 Bb6
7.e5 Ng4 8.h3 Nh6 9.d5
Ne7 10.d6 Ng6 11.Bg5 f6
12.exf6 gxf6 13.Qe2+ Kf8
and mate is swift!!
14.Bxh6 mate.

DIAGRAM 4.
1.e4 e5 2.Nf3 Nc6
3.Bc4 Bc5 4.c3 Nf6
5.d4 exd4 6.cxd4 Bb4+
7.Nc3 Nxe4 8.0-0 Bxc3
9.d5 Ne5 10.bxc3 Nxc4
11.Qd4 Ncd6 12.Qxg7 Qf6
13.Qxf6 Nxf6 14.Re1+
Kf8 15.Bh6+ Kg8 16.Re5
Nde4 Remove the guard
and win! 17.Nd2 d6 (if
17.....Nxd2 18.Rg5
mate)
18.Nxe4 dxe5
(18....Nxe4 19.Re8++)
19.Nxf6 mate.

DIAGRAM 5.

1.e4 e5 2.Nf3 Nc6
3.Bc4 Bc5 4.c3 Nf6 5.d4
exd4 6.cxd4 Bb4+ 7.Nc3
Nxe4 8.0-0 Bxc3 9.d5
Bf6 10.Re1 0-0 11.Rxe4
Ne7 12.d6 cxd6 13.Qxd6
Nf5 14.Qd5 d6 15.Bg5
Bxg5 16.Nxg5 Qxg5 and
mate occurs after
**17.Qxf7+ Rxf7 (17....Kh8
18.Qxf8 mate) 18.Re8
mate.**

DIAGRAM 6.

1.e4 e5 2.Nf3 Nc6
3.Bc4 Nf6 4.0-0 Nxe4
5.d4 d5 6.Bb5 Bd7
7.Bxc6 bxc6 8.Nxe5 f6
9.Qh5+ Ke7 10.Qf7+ Kd6
11.Bf4 g5 White wins
with **12.Nc4 mate.**

DIAGRAM 7.

1.e4 e5 2.Nf3 Nc6
3.Bc4 Nf6 4.d4 exd4
5.0-0 Nxe4 6.Re1 d5
7.Bxd5 Qxd5 8.Nc3 Qf5
9.Nxe4 Be6 10.Nxd4 Nxd4
11.Qxd4 h6 12.b3 a6
13.Bb2 a5 14.Rad1 f6
15.Qd7+ Bxd7 16.Nd6+ Kd8
and the mating attack
continues with **17.Nf7+
Kc8 18.Re8+ Bxe8
19.Rd8 mate.**

DIAGRAM 8.

1.e4 Nc6 2.Nf3 e5
3.Bc4 d6 4.0-0 f5 5.d3
Nf6 6.Nc3 h6 7.Nh4 Ne7
8.Nd5 Nfxd5 9.Qh5+ g6
10.Nxg6 Nf6 and mate in
two with **11.Nxe5+ Nxh5
12.Bf7 mate. or
11....Ng6 12.Qxg6+ Ke7
13.Qf7++**

DIAGRAM 9.

1.e4 e5 2.Nf3 Nc6
3.Bc4 d6 4.0-0 Nge7
5.Ng5 f6 6.Bf7+ Kd7
7.Qg4+ f5 8.exf5 h5 and
mate in three with
**9.f6+ hxg4 10.Be6+ Ke8
11.f7 mate.**

DIAGRAM 10.

1.e4 e5 2.Nf3 Nc6
3.Bc4 f6 4.Nh4 g5 and
Black is punished
quickly with 5.Qh5+ Ke7
6.Nf5 mate.

DIAGRAM 11.

1.e4 e5 2.Nf3 Nc6
3.Bc4 Bc5 4.d3 Nf6
5.Bg5 0-0 6.Nc3 d6
7.Nd5 Kh8 8.Bxf6 gxf6
9.Qd2 f5 10.Qh6 f6
11.Nh4 Rf7 12.Ng6+ Kg8
and White decoys the
Black Queen with
**13.Nxf6+ Qxf6 14.Qf8
mate.**

Diagram 12.

1.e4 e5 2.Nf3 Nc6
3.Bc4 Nf6 4.d4 exd4
5.e5 Ng4 6.Bxf7+ Kxf7
7.Ng5+ Kg8 8.Qxg4 Bb4+
9.c3 dxc3 and White
mates with **10.Qc4+ d5
(10....Kf8 11.Qf7 mate)
11.exd6(e.p.)+ Be6
12.Qxe6+ Kf8 13.Qf7
mate.**

DIAGRAM 13.

1.e4 e5 2.Nf3 Nc6
3.Bc4 Bd6 4.0-0 Nf6
5.Nc3 0-0 6.d3 Na5
7.Bg5 Nxc4 8.dxc4 Re8
9.a3 b6 10.Nd5 Be7
11.Nxe5 Nxd5 12.Qxd5
Bxg5 13.Nxf7 Bb7 and a
smothered mate follows,
**14.Nh6+ (dbl ch.) Kh8
15.Qg8+ Rxg8 16.Nf7
mate.**

DIAGRAM 14.

1.e4 e5 2.Nf3 Nc6 3.
Bc4 d6 4.d3 Bg4 5.Nc3
Nd4 6.Nxe5 Bxd1??
(Legal's Mate) **7.Bxf7+
Ke7 8.Nd5 mate.**

DIAGRAM 15.

1.e4 e5 2.Nf3 Nc6
3.Bc4 d6 4.d4 exd4
5.Nxd4 Nxd4 6.Qxd4 c6
7.0-0 Ne7 8.Re1 c5
9.Qc3 a6 10.Qb3 f6
11.Bf4 Nc6 12.Bf7+ Ke7
13.Nc3 Nd4 14.Qd5 Qc7
15.Rad1 Bd7 16.e5 dxe5

17.Rxe5+ fxe5 and
18.Bg5 mates.

DIAGRAM 16.

1.e4 e5 2.Nf3 Nc6
3.Bc4 Be7 4.d4 d6 5.h3
f5 6.d5 Nb8 7.Nc3 h6
8.exf5 Bxf5 9.Bd3 Qd7
10.g4 Bxd3 11.Qxd3 c6
12.Qg6+ Kf8 13.Be3 Nf6
14.g5 hxg5 15.Nxg5 Qe8
and mate in two with
**16.Ne6+ Kg8 17.Qxg7
mate.**

DIAGRAM 17.

1.e4 e5 2.Nf3 Nc6
3.Bc4 Bc5 4.d3 d6 5.Nc3
Bg4 6.Be3 Bxe3 7.fxe3
Nge7 8.0-0 Ng6 9.Qe1 a6
10.Qg3 Bxf3 11.Qxf3 f6
12.Qf5 Qe7 13.Nd5 Qd8
14.Qe6+ Nge7 and White
controls the light...
(squares, that is)
**15.Nxf6+ gxf6 16.Qf7+
Kd7 17.Be6 mate.**

DIAGRAM 18.

1.e4 e5 2.Nf3 Nc6
3.Bc4 Nf6 4.Ng5 Nxe4
5.Bxf7+ Ke7 6.d4 Nxd4
7.c3 Ne6 8.Bxe6 Nxf2
9.Qf3 Nxh1 10.Qf7+ Kd6
11.Ne4+ Kc6 12.Bd5+ Kb6
13.Bg5 Be7 14.Bxe7 Qe8
15.Bc5+ Ka6 16.Qf1+ b5
17.a4 c6 mate in three
starts with **18.Qxb5+!
cxb5 19.axb5+ Kxb5
20.c4 mate.**

DIAGRAM 19.

1.e4 e5 2.Nf3 Nc6
3.Bc4 Bc5 4.c3 Nf6
5.d4 exd4 6.cxd4 Bb4+
7.Nc3 Nxe4 8.0-0 Bxc3
9.d5 Bf6 10.Re1 Ne7
11.Rxe4 0-0 12.d6 Ng6
13.h4 Nxh4 14.Nxh4 Bxh4
15.Qh5 Bf6 and White
decoys the Queen from
protection of e8
**16.dxc7 Qxc7 17.Qxf7+
Rxf7 18.Re8 mate.**

DIAGRAM 20.

1.e4 Nc6 2.Nf3 e5
3.Bc4 Nf6 4.Ng5 Bc5
5.Nxf7 Bxf2+ 6.Kxf2
Nxe4+ 7.Kg1 Qh4 8.g3
Nxg3+ 9.Nxh8 Nxh1
10.Qf1 d6? 11.Qf7+ Kd8
12.Qf8+ Kd7 and White
lures the Black King
onto a mating square
**13.Be6+ Kxe6 14.Qf7
mate.**

DIAGRAM 21.

1.e4 e5 2.Nf3 Nc6
3.Bc4 Nf6 4.d4 exd4
5.0-0 Bc5 6.e5 d5
7.exf6 dxc4 8.Re1+ Kf8
9.Bg5 gxf6 10.Bh6+ Kg8
11.Nc3 dxc3?? and mate
in 3 follows that
blunder **12.Qxd8+ Nxd8
13.Re8+ Bf8 14.Rxf8
mate.**

DIAGRAM 22.

1.e4 e5 2.Nf3 Nc6
3.Bc4 Nf6 4.Ng5 d5
5.exd5 Nxd5 6.Nxf7 Kxf7
7.Qf3+ Ke6 8.Nc3 Nb4
9.a3 Nxc2+ 10.Kd1 Nxa1
11.Nxd5 Kd6 12.d4 exd4
13.Bf4+ Kc5 14.Ba2 a5
15.Bxc7 Qd7 16.Kd2 Nc2
17.Rc1 d3 and White
turns up the heat on the
"Fried Liver,"
**17.Rxc2+! dxc2 18.Qc3+
Kb5 19.Qc4++**

DIAGRAM 23.

1.e4 e5 2.Nf3 Nc6
3.Bc4 Nf6 4.d4 exd4
5.0-0 Bc5 6.e5 d5
7.exf6 dxc4 8.Re1+ Kf8
9.Bg5 gxf6 10.Bh6+ Kg8
11.Nxd4 Bxd4 12.c3 Be6
13.cxd4 Qxd4 14.Qh5 Ne5
15.Nc3 Qg4 16.Rxe5 fxe5
and mate is inevitable
**17.Nd5! Qxh5(17....Bxd5
18.Qxg4 mate) 18.Nf6
mate.**

Diagram 24.

1.e4 e5 2.Nf3 Nc6
3.Bc4 Bc5 4.0-0 Nf6
5.d4 exd4 6.e5 Ne4?
7.Bd5 f5 8.exf6 Nxf6
9.Bg5 h6 10.Re1+ Be7

11.Bxf6 gxf6 12.Nxd4
Nxd4   and Black pays
the price for his ruined
King-side **13.Qh5+ Kf8
14.Qf7 mate.**

DIAGRAM 25.

1.e4 e5 2.Nf3 Nc6
3.Bc4 Nf6 4.0-0 Be7
5.d4 exd4 6.e5 Ne4
7.Re1 Nc5 8.Nxd4 Ne6
9.Nf5 a6 10.Nxe7 Qxe7
11.a4 b6 12.Nc3 0-0
13.Nd5 Qd8 14.Qh5 Kh8
15.Nf6 gxf6 and mate
can't be stopped **16.Bd3
Ng5 17.Bxg5 fxg5
18.Qxh7 mate.**

DIAGRAM 26.

1.e4 e5 2.Nf3 Nc6 3.
Bc4 Bc5 4.b4 Bxb4 5.c3
Ba5 6.0-0 Nf6 7.d4
exd4 8.Ba3 d6 9.e5 dxe5
10.Qb3 Qd7 11.Re1 Qf5
12.Bb5 Nd7 13.Qd5
(trying for 14.Bxc6 bxc6
15.Qxa5) 13....Bb6
14.Nxe5 Ne7(14....Nxe5
15.Rxe5+ wins the Queen)
15.Nxd7 Qxd5 and White
mates with **16.Nf6+
Kd8 or Kf8 17.Bxe7
mate.**

DIAGRAM 27.

1.e4 e5 2.Nf3 Nc6 3.
Bc4 Bc5 4.b4 Bxb4 5.c3
Ba5 6.0-0 Nf6 7.d4
exd4 8.Ba3 d6 9.e5 dxe5
10.Qb3 Qd7 11.Re1 Qf5
12.Bb5 Nd7 13.Qd5 Bxc3
14.Nxc3 dxc3 15.Nxe5
Ne7 16.Nxd7 Qxd5 look
familiar? **17.Nf6+ Kd8
or Kf8 17.Bxe7 mate.**

DIAGRAM 28.

1.e4 e5 2.Nf3 Nc6 3.
Bc4 Bc5 4.b4 Bxb4 5.c3
Ba5 6.0-0 Nf6 7.d4 0-0
8.dxe5 Nxe4 9.Bd5 Nxc3
10.Nxc3 Bxc3 11.Ng5
Nxe5 12.Qh5 h6 13.f4
Bxa1 14.fxe5 Qe7
15.Nxf7 Qc5+ 16.Kh1 Qxd5
17.Nxh6+ gxh6? and now
White wins **18.Qg6+ Kh8
19.Rxf8+ Qg8 20.Qxg8
mate.**

DIAGRAM 29.

1..e4 e5 2.Nf3 Nc6
3. Bc4 Bc5 4.b4 Bxb4
5.c3 Ba5 6.0-0 Nf6
7.d4 0-0 8.dxe5 Nxe4
9.Bd5 Nxc3 10.Nxc3 Bxc3
11.Ng5 Nxe5 12.Qh5 h6
13.f4 Bxa1 14.fxe5 Qe7
15.Nxf7 Qc5+ 16.Kh1 Qxd5
17.Nxh6+ Kh8 and still
mate in two **18.Nf5+ Kg8
19.Ne7 mate.**

DIAGRAM 30.

1.e4 e5 2.Nf3 Nc6 3.
Bc4 Bc5 4.b4 Bxb4 5.c3
Ba5 6.0-0 d6 7.d4 Bg4
8.Qb3 Qd7 9.Ng5 Nd8
10.dxe5 dxe5 11.Ba3 Nh6
12.f3 Bb6+ 13.Kh1 Bh5
14.Rd1 Qc8 15.Rxd8+
Qxd8 16.Nxf7 Qh4
17.Qb5+ c6 and the
attack ends with
**18.Qxe5+ Kd7 19.Qe6+
Kc7 20.Bd6 mate.**

PAGE 95

1..1.Kc7+! Ka7 2.b6++
2...1.Rc7 K moves
2.Rb7 (double attack)
3...1.Bxg6+ wins the
Queen
4...1.Rh5+ Kg8 2.Rh8++
5...1.Rf1! (cross-pin)
6...1.Nxc6+

PAGE 96

1..1.Ba2 bxa 2.Nbc2++
  or 1.Ba2 b2 2.Nac2++
2...1.Qxa2
3...1.Qxg7+ Bxg7
2.Nf6++
4...1.Qa3++ is faster
than 1.Bg5+ Nf6 2.exf6+
gxf 3.Qa3++
5...1.Ke2 (1.Bxd3+ is
the slow route)
6...1.Qa1 Kh7 2.Nf5++
or 1.Qa1 Kg8 2.Ne6++

1..1.Ke6
2..1.Rf7! threatens
2.Rxe7 and 2.Qxb7++ (if
1....Rd8 2.Qxa5+ wins)
3..1.Ke3 wins the
Knight
4..1.c4 Kg8 2.Ke2!
5..1.Ne6++
6..1.Kf8 any move for
Black 2.Rh5++ or
1.Bc3+ also leads to
mate.

1..1.gb=R Ka2 2.Ra8++
2..1.Qd7! threatens
2.Qe8++ and 2.Qxd8+
3..1.Qc4++
4..1.Nf5+ Ke8
2.Nxg7++
5..1.Bf6! and the
Queen is trapped
6..1.Qxf3! Qxg5?
2.Qxa8+ not 1.Bxf6
Bxd8

1..1.Rxf7! not
1.Bxf7+
2..1.Nf7+ Kg7 2.Bh6++
3..1.Rd8! Qxd8 2.Qh8+
wins the Queen
4..1.Rf1! the cross-
pin
5..1.Bg4 Qxg4 2.Rhg1
pins the Queen to the
mate at g7
6..1.Bg6++

# 1..1.Qc4+ Qxc4
2.g8=Q+ wins the Queen
# 2..1.Qg5++
# 3..1.Qxe3+ Kxe3
2.Bf2+ wins
4..1.Rxd7 Qxd7 2.Nh6+
and a discovered attack
on the Queen
5..1.Nd6 a8=Q 2.Nf7++
6..1.Rh8+ Kxh8
2.Bxg7+ and the Queen is
hanging

1..1.Rxd5+ cxd5
2.Nd3+ exd3 3.f4++
2..1.Nh6+ Kh8 2.Nxf7+
Kg8 3.Rxg7++

3..1.Qxh7+ Kxh7
2.hxg5+ Kg6 or Kg8
3.Ne7++
4..1.Nc7+ Kf8 2.Qd8+
Bxd8 3.Re8++
5..1.Nxa7+ Bxa7
2.Qxc6+ bxc6 3.Ba6++
6..1.Rg8+ Kxg8 2.Rg1+
Kh8 3.Bf6++

1..1.Qxf6+ gxf6
2.Bh6+ Qg7 3.Rxf6++
2..1.Nh5+ Rxh5
2.Rxg6+ Kxg6 3.Re6++
3..1.Bc2+ Ke6 2.Rxh6+
f6 3.Ng5++
4..1.Qxe4+ Kxe4
2.Nc3+ Kf5 3.Rf1++
5..1.Ng6+ Kg8 2.Nxf6
Qxf6 3.Qf8++
6..1.Ne5+ Nxf7 2.Be2+
Bg4 3.Bxg4++

1..1.Rxb6+ Qxc6
2.Rxa2+ Qa4 3.Rxa4++
2..1.Re8+ Bf8 2.Bh6
Qxd5 3.Rxf8++
3..1.Rc8+ Nxc8
2.Qxb7+ Kxb7 3.Bd5++
4..1.Bb5+ axb5
2.Qxb5+ Ke6 3.Nd8++
5..1.f8=Q+ Bxf8
2.Rf7+ Nxf7 3.Re6++
6..1.Bc2+ Ke6 2.Rxh6+
f6 3.Ng5++

1..1.Bf6! gxf6 2.Kf8
g5 3.Nf7++
2..1.Rb7 e2 2.Rb8+
Rxb8 3.Nc7++
3..1.Rb8+ Ke7 2.Bc5+
Kf7 3.Rf8++
4..1.Ne7+ Kh8 2.Rxh7
Kh7 3. Rh5++ or Qh3++
5..1.Qxe6+ fxe6
2.Nb6+ axb6 3.Bxe6++
6..1.Rb7+ Bxb7 2.Nc2+
Nxc2 3.Rb5++

1..1.Qd3+ Kc5 2.Qd4+
Kb5 3.Qb4++
2..1.Rb1+ Ka7 2.Qd4+
Qxd4 3.Nxc6++
3..1.Nh5+ Rxh5
2.Rxg6+ Kxg6 3.Re6++

4..1.Ng3+ Kh2 2.Rh1+
Bxh1 3.Nf1++
5..1.Qxf7+ Kxf7
2.R1h7+ Ke8 3.Bxg6++
6..1.Qb6+ Nxb6 2.Bc3+
Nb4 3.Bxb4++

1..1.Rh8+ Kxh8
2.Qxf8+ Rg8 3.Qh6++
2..1.Qxg7+ Kxg7
2.Nf5+ Kg8 3.Nh6++
3..1.Ng6+ Kxh7
2.Nxf8+ Kh8 3.Qh7++
4..1.Rf8+ Bxf8 2.Qf7+
Kd8 3.Qd7++
5..1.Bf6+ Rxf6 2.g3+
Kh3 3.Qh5++
6..1.g7+ Rxg7 2.Qh5+
Rh7 3.Qxh7++

1..1.Qxh4 Bxh4 2.Bg7+
Kh5 3.g4++
2..1.Re8+ Rxe8 2.Qg4+
Qxg4 3.Nf6++
3..1.Rxg7+ Kxg7
2.Bh6+ Kxh6 3.Qg5++
4..1.Re7+ Kf8 2.Re8+
Kxe8 3.Qe7++
5..1.Bxh7+ Nxh7
2.Qxh7+ Kf8 3.Qh8++
6..1.Ne7+ Nxe7
2.Bxh7+ Qxh7 3.Qxh7++

1..1.Qg5+ Kf7 2.Rd7+
K moves 3.Qd8++
2..1.Rg7! any Knight
move 2.Rg8+ Rxg8
3.Nf7++ or 1...R moves
2. Nf7++
3..1.f5+ exf5 or Qxf5
2.Qxh6+ gxh6 3.Rag8++
4..1.Ng5+ fxg5 or hxg5
2.Re7+ K moves 3.Qxg7++
5..1.Rb7+ Kg8 2.Rxb8+
Nf8 3.Rxf8++
6..1.Ne8+ Ke5 2.Qg3+
Ke4 3.Nf6++ or 2.Qg7+
or 2.Qh8+ Ke4 3.Qd4++

1..1.Qe7+ Kb6 2.Qxd6+
K moves 3.Qc6++
2..1.Bb6+ axb6
2.Ndxf7+ Kc7 3.Qd6++ or
2.....Ke8 3.Qd8++
3..1.Ng6+ fxg6 2.Bxg6
any move 3.Re8++ or
1.Ng6+ Kg8 2.Re8+ Kh7
3.Rxh8++
4..1.h5+ Kh6 2.Nxe6+
g5 3.hxg6(e.p.)++ or
2.....Kh7 3.Qxg7++
5..1.Ng4+ hxg4 2.Be5+
Kxe5 3.Qd4++ or
1.....Kg7 2.Qh7++ or
1.....Ke7 2.Qd6++
6..1.Qd8+ Kxd8 2.Ba5+
K moves 3.Rd8++

1..1.N5f6+ gxf6
2.Bh6+ Qg5 3.Nxf6++ or
2.....hxg4 3.Nxf6++
2..1.Rd8+ Kf7 2.Bc4+
Be6 3.Nxe5++ or
2.....Qe6 3.Nxe5++
3..1.Qd8+ Kxd8 2.Bg5+
Ke8 3.Rd8++ or
2.....Kc7 3.Bd8++
4..1.Nd8+ Kh8 (1...Nd5
2.Qf8++) 2.Qf8+ Ng8
3.Qxg8++ or 3.Nf7++
5..1.Qe6! Nxe6 or Rxe6
2.Nhg6+ Kg8 3.Rh8++ or
1.Qe6 Qxg2+ 2.Nxg2++ or
1.Qe6 Bxe6 2.Nf5+ Kg8
3.Ne7++
6..1.Be4! Rxe4 2.h3+
Kg3 3.Rf3++ or 1.Be4
Bxe4 2.h3+ Kg3 3.Be1++

1..1.e4 e5 2.Nf3 Nc6
3.Bb5 Nf6 4.0-0 Nxe4
5.Re1 Nd6 6.Nxe5 Be7
7.Bf1 0-0 8.d4 Nf5 9.c3
d5 10.Qd3 Re8 11.f4 Nd6
12.Re3 Na5 13.Nd2 Nf5
14.Rh3 Nh4 15.g4 Ng6
16.Rh5 Nc6 17.Ndc4! dxc4
**and White shocks Black
with 18.Qxg6 hxg6
19.Nxg6 fxg6 20.Bxc4+
Kf8 21.Rh8++ or
[18...fxg6 19.Bxc4+ Kf8
(19...Kh8 20.Ng6++)
20.Nxg6+ hxg6 21.Rh8++]
or [18...h6 19.Qxf7+
Kh8 (19...Kh7 20.Rxh6+**

Kxh6 21.Qg6++) 20.Rxh6+
gxh6 21.Ng6++]
2..1.e4 e5 2.Nf3 Nc6
3.Bb5 a6 4.Bxc6 dxc6
5.0-0 Qd6 6.Na3 b5 7.Nb1
Ne7 8.a4 Ng6 9.d4 Bg4
10.axb5 cxb5 11.h3 Bxf3
12.Qxf3 Qxd4 13.Rd1 Qb6
14.Nc3 c6 15.h4 Nxh4
16.Qg4 Be7 17.Qd7+ Kf8
18.Be3 Be5 **and the
overloaded Black Queen
is the target...19.Rxa6!
Rxa6 20.Bxc5+ Qxc5
21.Qd8++ or (19...Qxa6
20.Bxc5+ Kg8 21.Qd8+
Rxd8 22.Rxd8++) or
(19...Qb8 20.Bxc5+ Kg8
21.Rxa8 wins)**
3..1.e4 e5 2.Nf3 Nc6
3.Bb5 f6 4.0-0 Nge7
5.Nh4 a6 6.Bxc6 Nxc6
7.Qh5 g6 8.Nxg6 Rg8
9.Nxe5+ Ke7 10.Qf7+ Kd6
11.Nc4+ Kc5 **and White
wins with 12.Qd5+ Kb4
13.c3+ Ka4 14.b3++**
4..1.e4 e5 2.Nf3 Nc6
3.Bb5 Qe7 4.Nc3 Nf6 5.d4
Nxd4 6.Nxd4 exd4 7.Qxd4
c6 8.0-0 cxb5 9.Nxe5 Ke7
10.Nd5 Qd8 11.Qc3 Rb8
12.Nc7+ Ke7 13.Re1 d5
14.exd6+ Kd7 15.Qh3+ Kc6
16.Qf3+ Kd7 17.Qf5+ Kc6
**and mate in 2 with
18.Qb5+ Kxd6 19.Bf4++**
5..1.e4 e5 2.Nf3 Nc6
3.Bb5 Nge7 4.0-0 g6 5.d4
Bg7 6.dxe5 Nxe5 7.Nxe5
Bxe5 8.Bh6 Bxb2 9.Nd2 c6
10.Rb1 Bd4 11.Nc4 Bc5
**and White follows with
12.Qd4! Bxd4 13.Nd6++
or 12...Rg8 13.Qxc5
wins.**
6..1.e4 e5 2.Nf3 Nc6
3.Bb5 a6 4.Ba4 d6 5.c4
f5 6.d4 fxe4 7.Nxe5 dxe5
8.Qh5+ Ke7 9.Bxc6 Qxd4
10.Qe8+ Kd6 11.Be3 Qxc4
12.Nc3 Bg4 **and mate in
two...13.Rd1+ Bxd1
14.Qd7++ (13...Qd3
14.Nxd4++)**

1..1.Nd5 Qd8
2.Bxc6(removes the
defender) bxc6 3.Nxb4

2..1.Bd6!! a double
attack that threatens
Rf8++ and Qxe6
3..1.Bf7+ Kxf7 2.Rg7+
Ke6 3.Re7++
4..1.Nf7++
5..1.Ne5+ Ke6 2.Qg8+
K moves 3.Qxb3
6..1.Qg8+ Ke7 2.Qe6+
Kf8 3.Qd6++

1..1.Rc8! if
1.....Rxa7? 2.Kb6+ wins
2..1.Bxf8 Kxf8 2.Bxf7
Kxf7 3.Nd6+
3..1.Nd8+ Rxd8
2.Qxe7+ Kg8 3.Qxd8+
4..1.Rxb7+ Nxb7
2.Na6++
# 5..1.Qe5+! Qxe5
2.exd8=Q++ or 1.....Kc8
2.Qxg5+ wins
6..1.Rd5! exd5
2.Qxd8+ Re8 3.Qxe8++ or
1.....Qxd5 2.Qf6++ or
1.....Rxd5 2.Qf8++

1..1.Ra7+ Re7 (if
1.....Kg8 2.Ra8)
2.Qe6! wins the rook
2..1.Nxc7 if 1...Qxc7
2.Bxe6+ Bxe6 3.Qxc7
3..1.Rxe6 Rxe6
(1...Qxe6 2.Rxh6 and
black is in trouble)
2.b6+ Kxb6 attracting
the King into a cross-
pin 3.Rh6 (not
2.....Kb8 3.Rh8+ and
White eventually mates)
4..1.Qh5+ wins
5..1.Re5+ Kf7 2.Qxd7+
6..1.Ne7+ Kh8 2.Nxc6
Bxc6 3.Nxc6 forks the
Rook & Queen

PAGE 115
1..1.Qd8+ Kxd8 2.Bg5+ Ke8 3.Rd8+ (Morphy's Mate)
2..1.Qf6++
3..1.Nd6++
4..1.Bf5! Ra5 (actually, any Black move loses) 2.Ne4++ or 2.Ne6++
5..1.Ng8+ Kxh5 2.Rh2++ or 1.Nf5+ Kxh5 2.Rh2++
6..1.Qb7+ Ke8 2.Qe7++ or 1.Qb7+ Qc7 2.Bxc6++

PAGE 116
1..1.Qe5++
2..1.Qe4+! Kxe4 2.Nc3++ or 1.Nc3+ Ne3 2.Qe4++
3..1.Qxh7+ Kxh7 2.Rh5+ Kg8 3.Rh8++
4..1.Rh5+ Kg7 2.Rxg6++ (discovered & double check)
5..1.Bh3+ Kf4 2.Ne4++
6..1.Qxd5+ exd5 2.Bb6+ axb6 3.Re8++ or 2....Rc7 3.Re8++

PAGE 117
1..1.Rxh7+ Kxh7 2.Qh5++
2..1.Qh7+ Kxf6 2.Qxh6++ or 1.....Kf8 2.Qg8++
3..1.Qb7++
4..1.Nh6+ gxh6 2.Rg4+ Kh8 3.Rxf8++
5..1.Qf5+ Kh6 2.Nxf7+ Rxf7 or Kg7 3.Qg6++ or 1.....Kh4 2.Nf3+ Kg3 3.Qh3++
6..1.hxg6+ Kg8 2.Rh8++

PAGE 118
1..1.Qxg7+ Qxg7 2.Rxf8+ Bg8 3.Rxg8++
2..1.Be6+ Kxe6 or Nxe6 or Ke8 2.Qf7++
3..1.Re8+ Bxe8 2.Rd8++
4..1.Ne6+ Bxe6 2.Bh6++
5..1.Qxf5+ Kd4 2.Be3+ Kxe3 3.Qf2++
6..1.Nd7++

PAGE 119
1..1.Rh8+ Kxh8 2.Rf8+ Kh7 3.Qh3++
2..1.Ng6+ hxg6 2.Qh3++
3..1.Qc5+ dxc5 2.Rd8++
4..1.Nd6++

PAGE 119...cont.
5..1.Nxd6++
6..1.Qh7+ Kxh7 2.Re7+ Kh8 3.Rh7++

PAGE 120
1..1.Bf5++
2..1.Qh3+ Nh4 (1. Kg5 2.Qg4+ Kh6 3.Qh5++) 2.Qxh4+ Kg6 3.Qh5++
3..1.Rxg7+ Kh8 2.Rg8+ Kxg8 3.Rg1++
4..1.Qxa6+ Kb8 2.Qxb7++ or 1.Qd5 any move 2.Qxb7++ or 2.Qd8++
5..1.Qh5 Rf6 2.Qh7+ Kf8 3.Qh8++
6..1.Rg8+ Qxg8 2.Qxh6+ Qh7 3.Qxh7++

PAGE 121
1..1.Bf8++
2..1.Rh5++
3..1.Nd6++
4..1.Bxd6++
5..1.Bg5++
6..1.Rg6++

PAGE 122
1..1.g8=N++
2..1.Bf6++
3..1.Rf7++
4..1.Bf6++
5..1.Qxh5++
6..1.Rg6++

PAGE 123
1..1.Nf7++
2..1.Bd7++
3..1.Qh3++
4..1.Re7++
5..1.Rg8++
6..1.Ne7++

PAGE 124
1..1.Qc6++
2..1.Bxh6++
3..1.Nxg7++
4..1.Ng6++ or 1.Rxf7++
5..1.Qb3++
6..1.Bb5++

PAGE 125
1..1.Qg8++
2..1.Bf4++
3..1.Bg6++
4..1.Qb7++
5..1.Nc7++
6..1.Qf3++

PAGE 126
1..1.Qa8++
2..1.Qb8++
3..1.Qh6++
4..1.Qa8++
5..1.f8=N++
6..1.Kf2++

PAGE 127
1.1.Nf7+ Kf5 2.g4++
2.1.Rg7+ Ke8 2.Nf6++
3.1.Ng3+ Kg1 2.Qf1++
4.1.Qd8+ Kxd8 2.Rd6++
5.1.Qb5+ Rxb5 2.Nc6++ or 1.... Kxb5 2.Rxb3+
6.1.Qc5+ Kxc5 2.Nxe6++

PAGE 128
1..1.Bf8+! Rxf8 (1...Kh5 2.Rxh7++) 2.Rd3! any move 3.Rh3++
2..1.Re5! Rxe5 2.Bxe5 and if Black moves the Bishop 3.Bc3++ and if 2....b5 3.Bc7++ if Black plays 1....Bd1 2.Rxc5 bxc5 3.Bc7++ Black could play 1....Rb5 and only lose a rook.
3..1.Qxd7+ Rxd7 2.Nc7+ Rxc7 3.Rd8++ (a variation on Morphy's mate)
4..1.Re6!! (threatening Rf6++ or Nxh6++) Nxe6 2.Bd3++
5..1.b4! Qd8 2.Qxf6+ Kxf6 (if 2.Kh6 3.Bb2 still leads to mate) 3.Bb2++
6..1.Qa7! (to decoy the Black Queen) Qa5 2.Qxa6 and Black must lose at least the rook.

\# 1..1.Ree5 fxe5 2. Bh7++
\# 2..1.Kg3 Kf5 2. Re6++
\# 3..1.d6 Bd7 2.Nf7++
  or 1.d6 Rd7 2.Ne6++
  other solutions are possible.
\# 4.. O-O R moves 2. Qf8++
\# 5..1.Ra1 Kd3 2.Ra3++
or 1.Ra1 Kb2 2.Bd4++
\# 6..g7=B Nh6 2.Qxg7++

\# 1..1.e8=B N moves 2.Bh5++ or Bb5++
\# 2..1.O-O-O B moves 2. RD8++ or Rh1++
\# 3..1.Ra1 Re1 2.Rf2++
  or 1.Ra1 R moves anywhere else 2.Ne3++
\# 4..1.Qe7 f6 2.Qxh7++
  or 1.Qe7 Kh6 or any other move 2.Qg5++
\# 5..1.Qa7 Kd8 2.Qd7++ or 1… Kf8 2.Qf7++
\# 6..1.Qe8 Kg5 2.Qb5++

\# 1..1.c8=R Ka6 2.Ra8++
\# 2..1.Qc2 Ka2 2.Qa4++ or 1.Qc2 b1=Q 2.Nxb1++
\# 3..1.Rce2 Nd2(to prevent the Bishop mate) 2.Re3++
\# 4..1.Kc8 Ka5 2.Nc4++ or 1.Kc8 Ka7 2.Bc5++
\# 5..1.Qb4 Kxd5 2.Qc5++ or 1.Qb4 Kxf5 2.Qxe4++
\# 6..1.Qe7 Kg8 2.Qe8++ or 1.Qe7 Bg6 2.Qf8++

\# 1..1…   Qa4+ 2.Kb1 2.Qd1+ etc.
\# 2..1.Qg5+ Kh8 2.Qf6+ etc.
\# 3..1.Re8+ Ka7 2.Rd7+ etc.
\# 4..1. … Nb3+ 2.Ka2 Nxc1+ 3.Ka1 etc.
\# 5..1.Qh4+ Q2h2 2.Qe4 Q1g2 3.Qe1+ etc.
\# 6..1. …Qf4+ 2.Kg2 Qc1+ etc.
        or !. … Qf4+ 2.g3 Qxf3+ 3.Kh1 Qf1+ etc.

Corrrections to the Answer Key

p.22 #5 2.Nxb4 should be Nxb7
p.30 #1 2.Qh6++ should be 2.Qh7++
p.55 #4 1.Qf3 any black move should be 1.Qf3+ Kxh4
p.57 #1 1.Qf7+ Bxf7 2.Ne8++ also works
p.64 #2 1.Bxd7++ is mate in one
p.64 #5 1.Qe7++ is mate in one
p.65 #2 1.Ra1 (or b1 or c1) Kg8(or pawn to h5 or h6) 2.Ra8++(or Rb8++ or Rc8++)
    also works
p.65 #3 1.Rf5+ Rg5 2.Rfxg5++ or Rgxg5++ or Nf4++, or if 1. … Bxf5 2.Nf4++
p.70 #4 1.Qf5++ is mate in one

Loyds and Mazes

The Triple Loyd

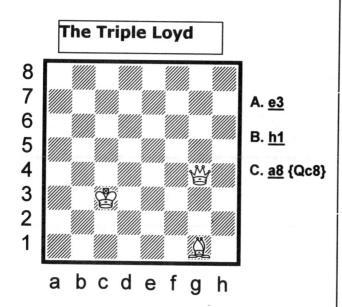

A. **e3**

B. **h1**

C. **a8** {Qc8}

The **triple loyd** was invented in 1866 by Sam Loyd the famous American chess composer known as "the Puzzle King". They are called triple because there are three parts.

In part A, you place the black king on the board so that he stands in checkmate. In part B, place him in stalemate. For part C, put the king down so that white has a mate in 1; then give the mating move.

This example is the original problem by Sam Loyd.

The Chessmaze

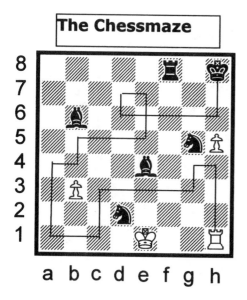

In a **chessmaze** only one white piece moves. The object is to capture the black king without taking any pieces or moving to any square where the white piece could be taken. A line can be drawn on the diagram to show the path of the piece.

In the example here, only the white rook moves. It is a *"maze in 15"* so the black king should be captured in fifteen moves or less.

These problems were composed by Canadian chess master Jeff Coakley, editor of *Scholar's Mate* magazine, where this material was first published. For more information on *Scholar's Mate*, Canada's chess magazine for kids, you can call (514) 845-8352 or write:

Scholar's Mate   Box 702 Station A   Montreal, Quebec, Canada H3C 2V2

The book, Chess Strategy For Kids, a collection of instructional articles from the magazine, is scheduled for publication in the summer of 2000.

TRIPLE LOYDS
(Place the Black King in: A) Checkmate B) Stalemate C) Mate in 1{Give the Mating Move})

Diagram 1

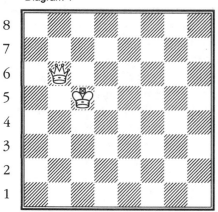

A. _____

B. _____

C. ____{____}

Diagram 2

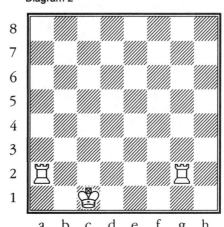

A. _____

B. _____

C. ____{____}

Diagram 3

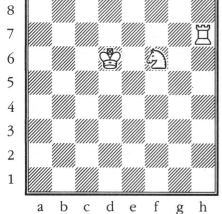

A. _____

B. _____

C. ____{____}

Diagram 4

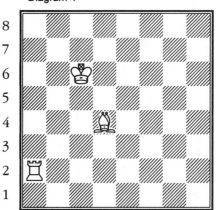

A. _____

B. _____

C. ____{____}

Diagram 5

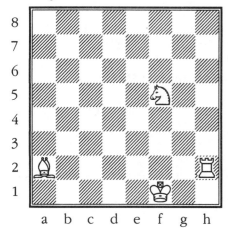

A. _____

B. _____

C. ____{____}

Diagram 6

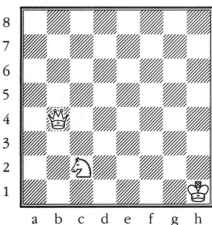

A. _____

B. _____

C. ____{____}

NAME_____Date_____Score___

TRIPLE LOYDS

(Place the Black King in: A) Checkmate B) Stalemate C) Mate in 1{Give the Mating Move})

Diagram 1

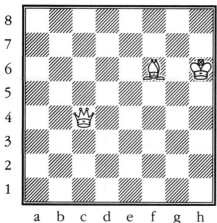

A. _____

B. _____

C. _____{_____}

Diagram 2

A. _____

B. _____

C. _____{_____}

Diagram 3

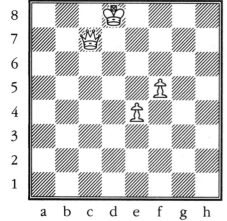

A. _____

B. _____

C. _____{_____}

Diagram 4

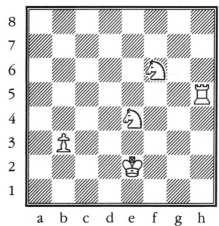

A. _____

B. _____

C. _____{_____}

Diagram 5

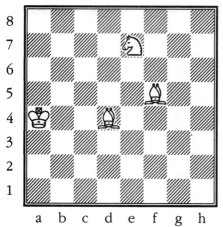

A. _____

B. _____

C. _____{_____}

Diagram 6

A. _____

B. _____

C. _____{_____}

TRIPLE LOYDS
(Place the Black King in: A) Checkmate B) Stalemate C) Mate in 1{Give the Mating Move})

Diagram 1

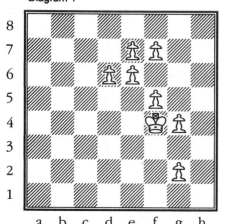

A. _____

B. _____

C. ___{___}

Diagram 2

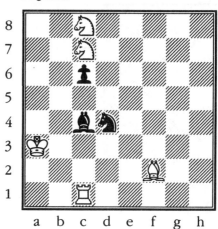

A. _____

B. _____

C. ___{___}

Diagram 3

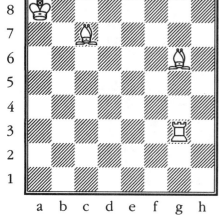

A. _____

B. _____

C. ___{___}

Diagram 4

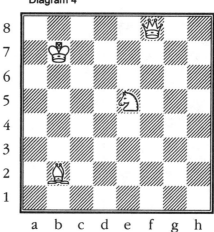

A. _____

B. _____

C. ___{___}

Diagram 5

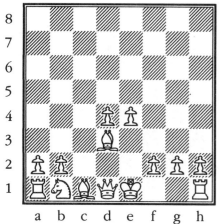

A. _____

B. _____

C. ___{___}

Diagram 6

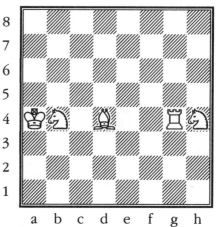

A. _____

B. _____

C. ___{___}

Canadian Corner, Page 4

TRIPLE LOYDS

(Place the Black King in: A) Checkmate B) Stalemate C) Mate in 1{Give the Mating Move})

Diagram 1

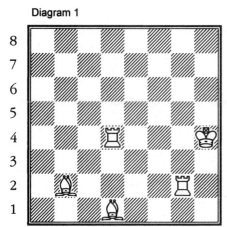

A. _____

B. _____

C. _____{_____}

Diagram 2

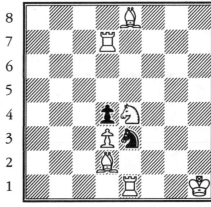

A. _____

B. _____

C. _____{_____}

Diagram 3

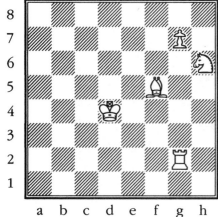

A. _____

B. _____

C. _____{_____}

Diagram 4

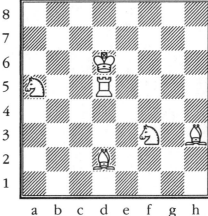

A. _____

B. _____

C. _____{_____}

Diagram 5

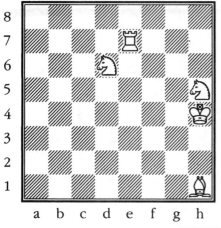

A. _____

B. _____

C. _____{_____}

Diagram 6

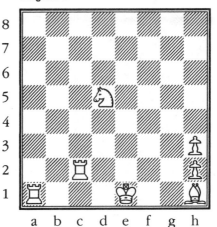

A. _____

B. _____

C. _____{_____}

Chessmaze

(Move only the designated white piece and try to capture the black king in the # of moves allowed.   Remember, you can't take any pieces or
move where the white piece can be taken.)

Diagram 1

MAZE in 7

BISHOP

Diagram 2

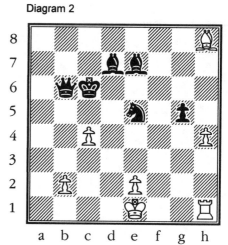

MAZE in 12

ROOK

Diagram 3

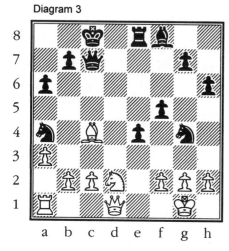

MAZE in 13

QUEEN

Diagram 4

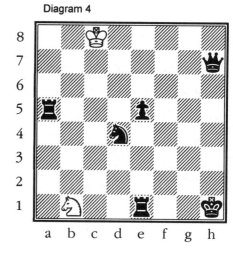

MAZE in 8

KNIGHT

Diagram 5

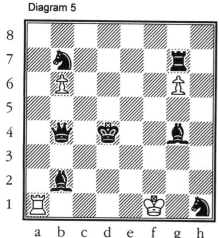

MAZE in 8

ROOK

Diagram 6

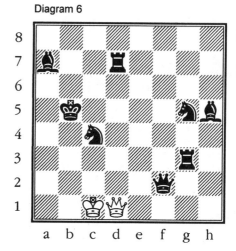

MAZE in 6

QUEEN

Chessmaze

(Move only the designated white piece and try to capture the black king in the # of moves allowed.   Remember, you can't take any pieces or move where the white piece can be taken.)

Diagram 1

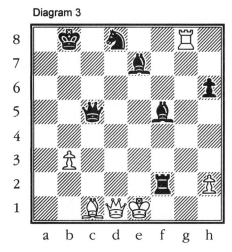

MAZE in 9

BISHOP

Diagram 2

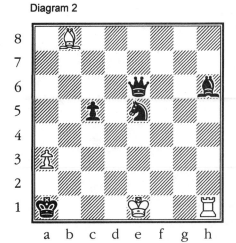

MAZE in 8

ROOK

Diagram 3

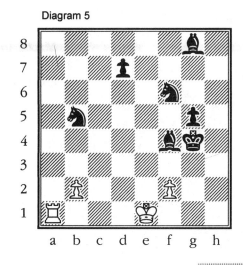

MAZE in 7

QUEEN

Diagram 4

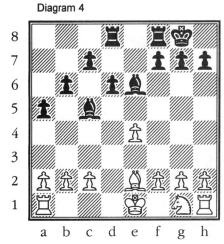

MAZE in 9

KNIGHT

Diagram 5

MAZE in 11

ROOK

Diagram 6

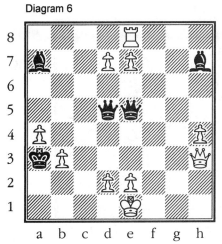

MAZE in 7

QUEEN

Canadian Corner, Page 7

Chessmaze

(Move only the designated white piece and try to capture the black king in the # of moves allowed.   Remember, you can't take any pieces or move where the white piece can be taken.)

Diagram 1

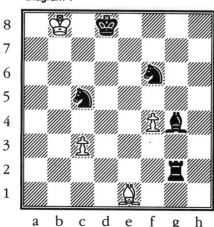

MAZE in 13

BISHOP

Diagram 2

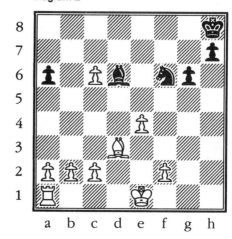

MAZE in 17

ROOK

Diagram 3

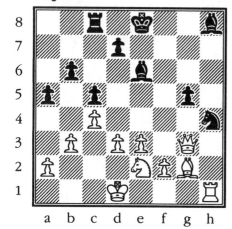

MAZE in 14

QUEEN

Diagram 4

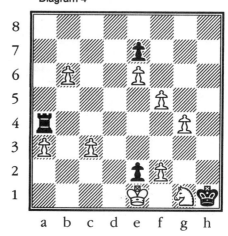

MAZE in 13

KNIGHT

Diagram 5

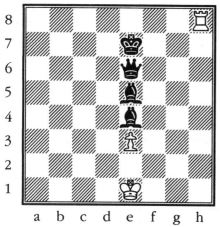

MAZE in 12

ROOK

Diagram 6

MAZE in 8

QUEEN

NAME_____Date_____Score___

Chessmaze

(Move only the designated white piece and try to capture the black king in the # of moves allowed.   Remember, you can't take any pieces or
move where the white piece can be taken.)

Diagram 1

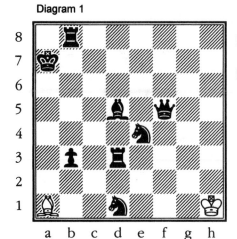

MAZE in 12

BISHOP

Diagram 2

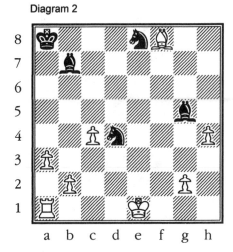

MAZE in 14

ROOK

Diagram 3

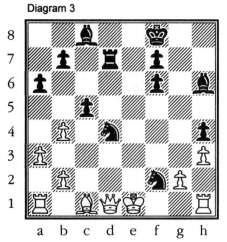

MAZE in 14

QUEEN

Diagram 4

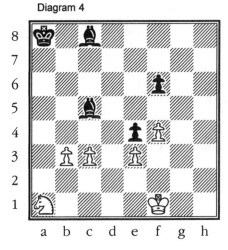

MAZE in 21

KNIGHT

Diagram 5

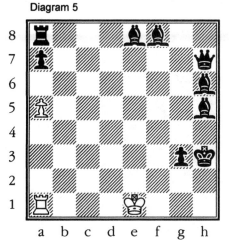

MAZE in 13

ROOK

Diagram 6

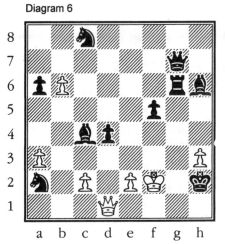

MAZE in 11

QUEEN

NAME_____Date_____Score___

CANADIAN CRUNCHES
(Mating combinations taken or derived from Canadian events)

#1 White to Move

1999 Canadian Championship
Spragett vs Gentes, mate in 2

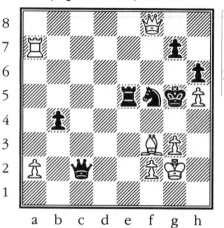

1. ____ ____

2. ____

#2 White to Move

1999 Canadian Championship
Duong vs Campbell, mate in 2

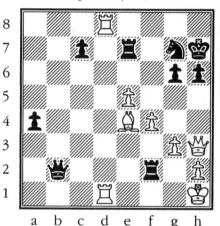

1. ____ ____

2. ____

#3 White to Move

1998 Quebec Women's Championship
Khaziyeva vs Mason, mate in 1

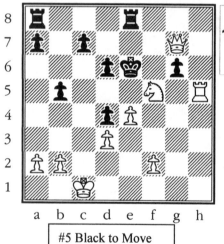

1. ____

#4 Black to Move

1998 Quebec Women's Championship
Bretine vs Khaziyeva, mate in 2

1. ____

2. ____ ____

#5 Black to Move

1998 Quebec Women's Championship
Veilleux vs Khaziyeva, mate in 2

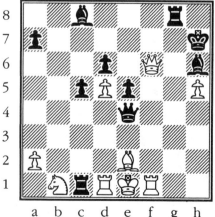

1. ____

2. ____ ____

#6 White to Move

1998 Canadian Youth Nationals
Khaziyeva vs Gushuliak, mate in 2

1. ____ ____

2. ____

Canadian Corner, Page 10

Canadian Combos
(White to Move, mate in two)

Diagram 1

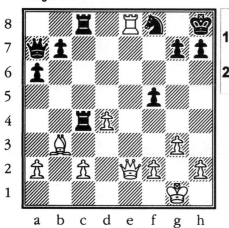

1. ____ ____

2. ____

Diagram 2

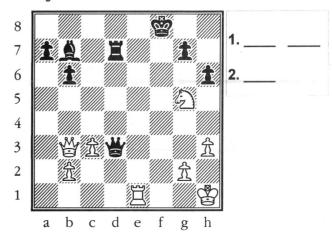

1. ____ ____

2. ____

Diagram 3

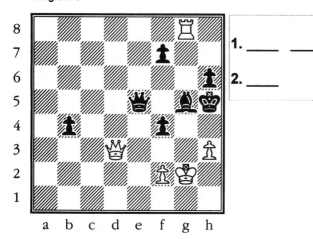

1. ____ ____

2. ____

Diagram 4

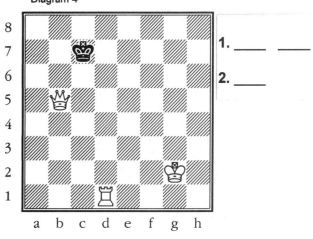

1. ____ ____

2. ____

Diagram 5

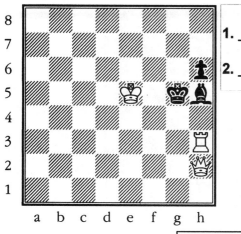

1. ____ ____

2. ____

Diagram 6

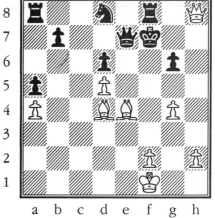

1. ____ ____

2. ____

Canadian Combos
(White to Move, mate in two)

Diagram 7

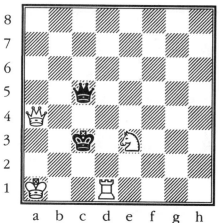

1. ____ ____

2. ____

Diagram 8

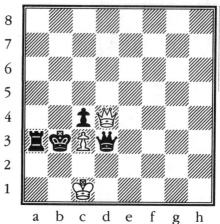

1. ____ ____

2. ____

Diagram 9

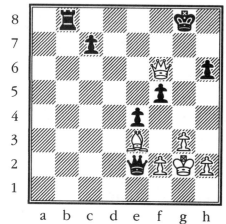

1. ____ ____

2. ____

Diagram 10

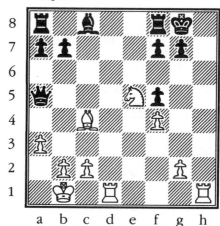

1. ____ ____

2. ____

Diagram 11

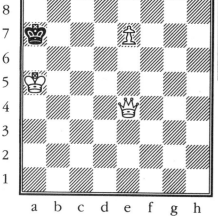

1. ____ ____

2. ____

Diagram 12

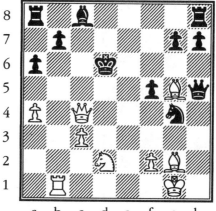

1. ____ ____

2. ____

Canadian Combos
(White to Move, mate in one)

Diagram 13

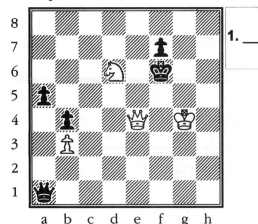

1. _____

Diagram 14

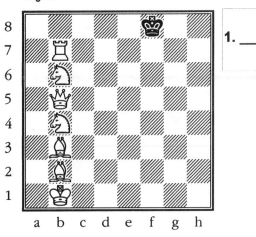

1. _____

Diagram 15

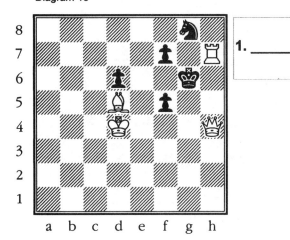

1. _____

Diagram 16

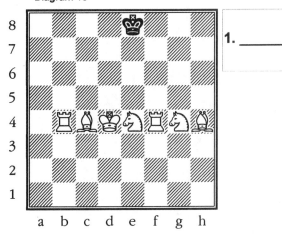

1. _____

Diagram 17

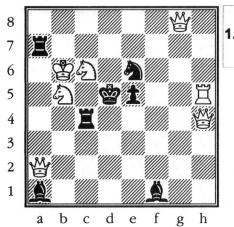

1. _____

Diagram 18

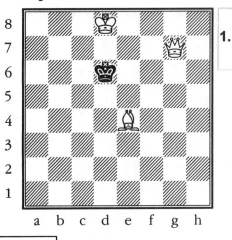

1. _____

Canadian Corner, Page 13

Canadian Combos
(White to Move, mate in one)

Diagram 19

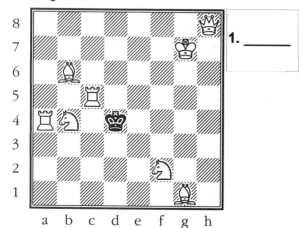

1. _____

Diagram 20

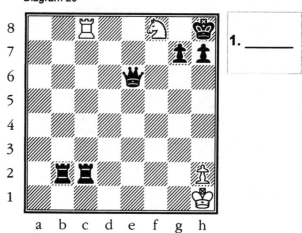

1. _____

Diagram 21

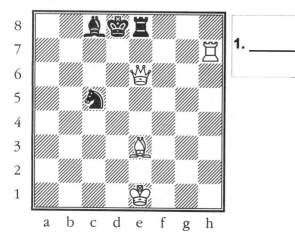

1. _____

Diagram 22

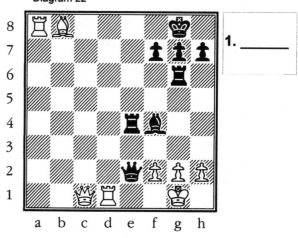

1. _____

Diagram 23

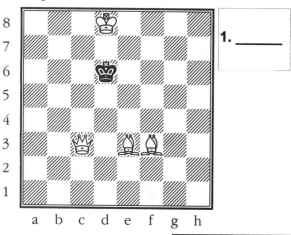

1. _____

Diagram 24

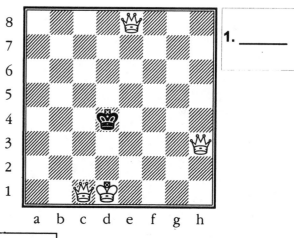

1. _____

Solutions: TRIPLE LOYDS

Canadian Corner, Page 2:

Diagram 1	Diagram 2	Diagram 3	Diagram 4	Diagram 5	Diagram 6
A. Ka6	A. Ka1	A. Kh8	A. Ka6	A. Kh8	A. Ka4
B. Ka8	B. Kh1	B. Kf8	B. Kh1	B. Ka1	B. Ka2
C. Ka4{ Qb4 }	C. Ke1{ Rg1 }	C. Kd8{ Rh8 }	C. Kc8{ Ra8 }	C. Kf8{ Rh8 }	C. Kf1{ Qe1 }

Canadian Corner, Page 3:

Diagram 1	Diagram 2	Diagram 3	Diagram 4	Diagram 5	Diagram 6
A. Kh8	A. Kd4	A. Kd6	A. Kh4	A. Kh8	A. Kf4
B. Ka3	B. Kf4	B. Ka8	B. Kf4	B. Ka2	B. Kh8
C. Ka5{ Bd8 }	C. Kh8{ Rg8 }	C. Kf6{ Qe7 }	C. Kd4{ Rd5 }	C. Ka6{ Bc8 }	C. Kh5{ Rh7 }

Canadian Corner, Page 4:

Diagram 1	Diagram 2	Diagram 3	Diagram 4	Diagram 5	Diagram 6
A. Ke8	A. Ka1	A. Kf4	A. Kd8	A. Kf4	A. Ke4
B. Kh4	B. Kc5	B. Kh4	B. Kh7	B. Kh4	B. Kc4
C. Kf6{ e8/N }	C. Ka5{ Be1 }	C. Ka6{ Bd3 }	C. Ke4{ Qf3 }	C. Kb4{ Bd2 }	C. Kb1{ Rg1 }

Canadian Corner, Page 5:

Diagram 1	Diagram 2	Diagram 3	Diagram 4	Diagram 5	Diagram 6
A. Kc3	A. Kf1	A. Kg8	A. Kc4	A. Kf4	A. Kf3
B. Ke3	B. Kh6	B. Ka1	B. Kh1	B. Kb8	B. Kb5
C. Kh8{ Rd7 }	C. Kb5{ Rd6 }	C. Kf6{ g8/N }	C. Ke4{ Ng5 }	C. Kf8{ Re8 }	C. Kg1{0-0-0}

Solutions: CHESSMAZES

Canadian Corner, Page 6:

DIAGRAM 1: Bc1 - a3 - b4 - e1 - h4 - e7 - f8 x h6
DIAGRAM 2: Rh1 - h2 - g2 - g3 - c3 - c1 - a1 - a8 - g8 - g7 - h7 - h6 x c6
DIAGRAM 3: Qd1 - b1 - a2 - b3 - h3 - h5 - g6 - h7 - g8 - d5 - d4 - a7 - a8 x c8
DIAGRAM 4: Nb1 - d2 - c4 - d6 - e8 - f6 - g4 - f2 x h1
DIAGRAM 5: Ra1 - a8 - h8 - h2 - c2 - c6 - f6 - f4 x d4
DIAGRAM 6: Qd1 - h1 - a8 - h8 - a1 - b1 x b5

Canadian Corner, Page 7:

DIAGRAM 1: Be1 - b4 - a3 - b2 - g7 - h6 - e3 - g1 - h2 x b8
DIAGRAM 2: Rh1 - h4 - a4 - a7 - h7 - h8 - d8 - d1 x a1
DIAGRAM 3: Qd1 - h5 - e8 - a4 - a1 - g7 - g3 x b8
DIAGRAM 4: Ng1 - f3 - d2 - b1 - c3 - b5 - a7 - c6 - e7 x g8
DIAGRAM 5: Ra1 - a8 - c8 - c2 - e2 - e7 - g7 - g6 - h6 - h1 - g1 x g4
DIAGRAM 6: Qh3 - f1 - f8 - h6 - a6 - c8 - c1 x a3

Canadian Corner, Page 8:

DIAGRAM 1: Be1 - h4 - g5 - h6 - f8 - d6 - e5 - d4 - e3 - c1 - a3 - b4 - a5 x d8
DIAGRAM 2: Ra1 - d1 - d2 - e2 - e3 - h3 - h1 - g1 - g5 - a5 - a4 - c4 - c3 - b3 - b7 - a7 - a8 x h8
DIAGRAM 3: Qg3 - h2 - g1 - e1 - d2 - c1 - a3 - a4 - b5 - a6 - b7 - a7 - a8 x h8
DIAGRAM 4: Ng1 - f3 - d2 - b3 - a1 - c2 - e3 - d5 - c7 - e8 - g7 - h5 - g3 x h1
DIAGRAM 5: Rh8 - h5 - g5 - g1 - f1 - f2 - d2 - d1 - c1 - c5 - a5 - a7 x e7
DIAGRAM 6: Qb1 - a1 - h8 - g8 - g2 - h3 - e3 - e7 x a7

Canadian Corner, Page 9:

DIAGRAM 1: Ba1 - g7 - h6 - c1 - a3 - e7 - h4 - e1 - a5 - c7 - h2 - g1 x a7
DIAGRAM 2: Ra1 - d1 - d3 - h3 - h1 - f1 - f7 - h7 - h8 - g8 - g6 - b6 - b4 - a4 x a8
DIAGRAM 3: Qd1 - a4 - a5 - b6 - a7 - b8 - h2 - g1 - f1 - c4 - a2 - b1 - h7 - h8 x f8
DIAGRAM 4: Na1 - c2 - e1 - g2 - h4 - g6 - h8 - f7 - d8 - c6 - a5 - c4 - b2 - d1 - f2 - h1 - g3 - h5 - g7 - e8 - c7 x a8
DIAGRAM 5: Ra1 - a2 - b2 - b3 - c3 - c4 - d4 - d5 - e5 - e6 - f6 - f1 - h1 x h3
DIAGRAM 6: Qd1 - e1 - a5 - a4 - e8 - d8 - h4 - h5 - f3 - a8 - b8 x h2

Solutions: CANADIAN CRUNCHES & COMBOS

PAGE 10
\# 1..1.Rxg7+ Nxg7   2.Qf4++
\# 2..1.Qxh6+ Kxh6   2.Rh8++
\# 3..1.Nxd4++
\# 4..1.Rxh2+ Kxh2   2.Qg2++
\# 5..1.Rxd1+ Kxd1   2.Qxb1++
   or 1.Rxd1+ Kf2   2.Qe3++ or
Rg2++
\# 6..1.Qh8+ Kf7   2.Qe8++
   or 1.Qh8+ Rg8   2.Qf6++

PAGE 11
\# 1..1.Qxc4 Rxc4   2.Rxf8++
   or 1.Qxc4 Rxe8   2.Qg8++
\# 2..1.Qg8+ Kxg8   2.Re8++
\# 3..1.Qf3+ Kh4   2.Qg4++
\# 4..1.Rd7+ Kc8   2.Qb7++
\# 5..1.Qa2 Kg4 or Bh8   2.Qg2++
   or 1.Qa2 Kg6 or Bd1   2.Qg8++
\# 6..1.Bxg6+ Kxg6   2.Qh5++

PAGE 12
\# 7..1.Ka2 Qc4+   2.Qxc4++
   or 1.Ka2 Qd5+   2.Nxd5++
   or 1.Ka2 Qb4   2.Qc2++
   or 1.Ka2 Qd4   2.Qxd4++
\# 8..1.Qb6+ Ka4   2.Qb4++
   or 1.Qb6+ other   2.Qb2++
\# 9..1.Qg6+ Kf8   2.Bc5++
   or 1.Qg6+ Kh8   2.Bd4++
\# 10..1.Ng6 any move 2.Rh8++
\# 11..1.Qh7 K moves 2.e8=Q++
\# 12..1.Qc5+ Kxc5   2.Be7++
   or 1.Qc5+ other   2.Qe7++

PAGE 13
\# 13..1.Ne8++
\# 14..1.Bg7++
\# 15..1.Bxf7++
\# 16..1.Bb5++
\# 17..1.Nb4++
\# 18..1.Qe7++

PAGE 14
\# 19..1.Nc2++
\# 20..1.Ng6++
\# 21..1.Qb6++
\# 22..1.Be5++
\# 23..1.Qf6++
\# 24..1.Qhd7++